DATE DUE

DEMCO, INC. 38-2931

Mental Health
in the
United States

A Fifty-Year History

Sponsored by

The New York State Association
for Mental Health

Mental Health
in the
United States

A Fifty-Year History

NINA RIDENOUR, PH.D.

Published for the COMMONWEALTH FUND by

HARVARD UNIVERSITY PRESS

Cambridge, Massachusetts, 1961

Published for The Commonwealth Fund
by Harvard University Press, Cambridge, Massachusetts
Distributed in Great Britain by Oxford University Press, London

For approximately a quarter of a century THE COMMONWEALTH
FUND, through its Division of Publications, sponsored, edited,
produced, and distributed books and pamphlets germane to its purposes and operations as a philanthropic foundation. Since July 1,
1951, HARVARD UNIVERSITY PRESS has been the Fund's pub-
lisher.

Library of Congress Catalog Card No. 61–11630

Printed in the United States of America

PREFACE

THIS account has been written out of the conviction that today there are many people interested in the mental health movement who have had little opportunity to hear about its history. Because it is possible to tell only a fraction of the mental health story in a publication of this length, stress throughout has been on origins, early developments, and "firsts." The plan followed has been to devote most space to the beginnings of various facets of the movement, especially to those earlier in time, less well-known, and about which information is less easily available. Then, the nearer to the present the story comes, the less space is given to each topic.

Although there are references to the present, this account makes no attempt to delineate the mental health movement as it is today. For information about the current status of such subjects as psychiatric research, therapy, professional training, clinical and hospital facilities, statistics, public education, citizen participation, and half a hundred other aspects of the movement, the reader is referred to the wealth of other published material now available.

The readers for whom this account is intended are those who already have some degree of concern about the subject and know at least something about it. More specifically, this is for the boards, staffs, volunteers, and members of mental health associations; for students in the medical, social, and behavioral sciences; and for professional workers in mental health and related fields. Hopefully, it may also prove useful to legislators and public officials charged with the responsibility for allocating funds and making policy decisions affecting the mental health effort.

The manuscript has had the benefit of constructive criticism from many generous people. Appreciation for their assistance is acknowledged on the last pages.

NINA RIDENOUR, PH.D.

Chappaqua, New York
September 27, 1960

CONTENTS

INTRODUCTION

IT GIVES me satisfaction to introduce this brief but important history of the mental health movement. This is a story of struggles and problems — many of them as yet unsolved — recited here round by round.

Nina Ridenour brings to her task a grasp of the subject and the sensitivity which come only with years of working and caring. Her extensive publications both in professional journals and for the popular press have already made her name known to most readers of this book. She has been part of many of the events she recounts here: first as a clinical psychologist during the early years of her professional career; then for many years as a member of the professional staff of mental health associations — local, state, national, and international; and more recently, both as participant and observer of the mental health scene from the special vantage point of a philanthropic desk.

Further progress in the difficult field of mental illness and mental health will come only when millions of Americans know enough, care enough, and are willing to work together hard enough to *make* it come. Those of us who are devoted to the cause need to take time now and then to review what has gone before. Dr. Ridenour has performed an extraordinarily useful and praiseworthy service in putting together this summary of some of the successes and failures of the past. This slight volume has much to teach us. I speed it on its way in the hope that it will find its mark among those who share with me the sense of urgency in striving to bring about better days ahead for the mentally ill and new gains for mental health.

WILLIAM C. MENNINGER, M.D., *President*
The Menninger Foundation

Mental Health
in the
United States

A Fifty-Year History

Backdrop: May 6, 1908

Forerunners and Beginnings

IT WAS the afternoon of May 6, 1908 that a little knot of people sat down together in a residence in New Haven, Connecticut, upon the invitation of Clifford Whittingham Beers — a young man with a remarkable history — to organize the Connecticut Society for Mental Hygiene, the first state association of its kind and the beginning of the organized mental health movement in America.

HOPES

The objectives of this pioneering little group have a familiar ring today: "To work for the conservation of mental health; to help prevent nervous and mental disorders and mental defects; to help raise the standards of care. . . . ; to secure and disseminate reliable information. . . ." — phrases which in the years since 1908 have, with minor variations, been repeated in the charters and by-laws of hundreds of mental health associations all over the world.

History does not tell us the extent to which the New Haven group shared the clarity of purpose and the high sense of destiny of their young founder (he had just turned 32) but Clifford Beers for one had no doubts about how he intended to proceed. According to his plan the Connecticut Society was not only to be the first in a long line of societies to follow, but also to serve as a pilot effort to provide experience in organizing. As soon as feasible he proposed to organize a national society — a plan he carried out to the letter nine months later, when on February 19, 1909, he invited a similar group of a dozen people to come together in New York City's Manhattan Hotel for the purpose of creating the National Committee for Mental Hygiene (now the National Association for Mental Health). His dreams for the future called for a growing network of state and local mental hygiene societies extending across the United States and eventually throughout the world, a conception which is gradually coming to fruition as the years roll by.

FIRSTS

From our vantage point of half a century later, we can look back on the period around 1908 as the time when an astonishing number of important "firsts" were taking place — events which would later be recognized as having tremendous significance for the mental hygiene movement.

In Chicago in 1908, for instance, Dr. William Healy was holding the first meetings to discuss the Juvenile Psychopathic Institute he was planning to start the following year, the first systematic effort at the psychiatric examination of juvenile offenders — actually the first child guidance clinic.

In Baltimore Mr. Henry Phipps had recently offered funds
to Dr. William H. Welch to build a psychiatric hospital on
the grounds of Johns Hopkins University — and the new
Henry Phipps Psychiatric Clinic, the first of its kind, was
just opening its doors with Dr. Adolf Meyer as medical
director. Up in the cold northern tip of New York State,
St. Lawrence State Hospital was starting a clinic "for advice and treatment of incipient mental cases" — the first
outpatient clinic in a state mental hospital. In Massachusetts the state legislature was in the process of passing an
appropriation for a psychopathic hospital to be built in
Boston — not the first psychopathic hospital, because that
had opened at the University of Michigan two years before
— but the first in a state hospital system and one which
was to train many of the leaders in psychiatry for the next
fifty years. And Clark University was getting ready to receive a visitor the following summer — Sigmund Freud —
whose publications, only recently translated into English,
were beginning to arouse heated arguments in this country.

In 1908 important things were happening that would
affect the mentally deficient too. That very year at the
Training School at Vineland, New Jersey, Dr. Henry H.
Goddard was starting to use a new test-scale devised by two
French psychologists, the Drs. Binet and Simon, who had
developed the valuable concept of "mental age." (The idea
of an "intelligence quotient" came later.) These tests, later
revised by Terman and known as the "Stanford-Binet"
(and more colloquially as "IQ tests") were the first important breakthrough in the description and classification of
intelligence. Thirty miles away from New York City (not
more than half a day's drive in one of the new-fangled
motor cars) in a beautiful spot above the Hudson River, an
institution was being built on the new "cottage system,"
the Eastern New York Custodial Asylum, scarcely recog-

nizable to us today under that name, but later as Letch-
worth Village to be known throughout the world as one
of the pioneering and progressive institutions for the mentally deficient.

Medical education in 1908 was a far cry from what it is
today. Most medical schools were still proprietary institutions — operated for profit — not yet connected with the
universities, and requiring almost nothing of students in
the way of academic background prior to admission. But
shortly, Abraham Flexner, under the auspices of the Carnegie Foundation for the Advancement of Teaching,
would produce his courageous report which, when it appeared in 1910, was to startle the entire educational world,
and later, with the backing of the Rockefeller Foundation,
was to become one of the forces revolutionizing all medical
education and therefore all psychiatric education, so that
eventually it would not be necessary for psychiatrists to
get their psychiatric training "by exposure" — as some of
the best of them were still doing in 1908. There was of
course not yet such a profession as "psychiatric social work"
although "charity workers" had long been concerned about
the mentally ill, and the first professional social work appointment in any state hospital had occurred just three
years before.

VOCABULARY

Their 1908 vocabulary sounds strange to us today. Although some people were waging war on the phrases "lunacy" and "lunatic asylum," "insane asylum" was still an
accepted term. (In 1844 when the "Original Thirteen"
had organized what is now the American Psychiatric Association, most of them were superintendents of "asylums,"
six of "lunatic asylums" and only two came from institutions which were called "hospitals.") In 1908 psychiatrists

were still widely called "alienists" because they specialized in "alienated minds." "Idiot" meant anybody who was mentally retarded, and "dementia praecox" had recently been adopted as a term for what is now called "schizophrenia."

LACKS

In 1908 nobody knew very much about the over-all picture of the mentally ill. There was a general idea of the approximate number of mental patients in institutions — probably about 180,000 it was thought. But almost nothing was known about costs or about "movement" of patients such as admissions, re-admissions, and discharges. There was no list of institutions in existence and no list of psychiatrists. There was no uniform system of reporting and indeed it would have been impossible at that time because there was no agreement on nomenclature. There was no central repository for information about mental patients because no agency, either voluntary or governmental, had yet been charged with the responsibility for collecting statistics. There were no minimum standards for the care of patients in institutions, and few laws for their protection either before commitment or after. There was no central place where one could find out about commitment laws of the various states (which differed greatly), or about the amount and kind of responsibility for institutional care of the mentally ill assumed by the various state governments or about administrative practices in mental hospitals. Clearly the new mental hygiene societies had their work cut out for them.

II

"... But It Is Not Fiction"

Clifford Beers and His Early Supporters

WHEN THE Connecticut group came together in May 1908, a recent event of special interest to them was the publication two months before of a book *A Mind That Found Itself* by their organizer. This was the story of Clifford Beers' three years in mental hospitals (1900–1903), what he experienced and observed, his recovery, and his determination to bring about changes.

THE BOOK

Any attempt at retelling Clifford Beers' story would be a transgression. His book, now in its thirtieth printing, is every bit as readable, and as moving, today as it was when it came off the press in 1908. It is doubtful whether anyone can understand the present-day mental health movement without being familiar with this piece of history.

When Beers had finished writing the book in 1906 and was looking about for backers of his ambitious reform plan, he took his manuscript to the distinguished Harvard psychologist, William James. At first Professor James said he would not have time to read it. But he did read it, quite promptly, and sent Beers an enthusiastic letter of approval, which Beers later said marked the turning point in his struggle for support. From 1906 on, William James was a source of great strength to Clifford Beers. He wrote letters to him and for him, became an honorary trustee of the National Committee for Mental Hygiene, gave money and solicited it, and was generous with his time and counsel. "It reads like fiction but it is not fiction," he wrote in the introduction to the first edition of the book.

RECOGNITION

But William James was only the first in a long, long line of notables who in the next thirty years were to heap encomiums on Clifford Beers and his work. "A unique human record . . . poignantly moving and inspiring," said Booth Tarkington in the introduction to the twenty-fifth anniversary edition of the book. "One of the most remarkable autobiographies ever written" — from Yale's C.-E. A. Winslow. "One of the great movements of all time" — from William H. Welch. "One of the most important in the world today" — from Harry Emerson Fosdick. "Work which will be one of the greatest achievements of this country and of this century" — from Adolf Meyer. "A name worthy to be remembered in all generations" — from Governor Wilbur Cross of Connecticut.

In 1933, some five hundred such letters were assembled by Dr. Welch in commemoration of the founding of the mental hygiene movement. These were put into a book that was edited by Governor Cross and entitled *Twenty-*

five Years After: Sidelights on the Mental Hygiene Movement and Its Founder, a stirring record of tribute. Many other honors in this country and in Europe were also conferred upon Beers before his death in 1943.

Clifford Beers had the temperament of a crusader. Although subject to swings of mood and not always easy to work with, he was ebullient, persuasive, enormously energetic, commanding in personality, and effective as an interpreter for the cause which held the center of his life. His record in raising funds during the early years of the National Committee is impressive today even without making allowance for the difference in the value of the dollar then and now.

FRIENDS AND ASSOCIATES

Mr. Beers gave credit on many occasions to many people for their assistance in launching the mental hygiene movement. Among those he singled out for special acknowledgment were his wife, Clara Louise Jepson Beers, who at the time of the present writing continues her lively interest in the mental health movement; Victor Morris Tyler, boyhood friend, who lent Beers the money to keep him going during the first few arid years while he was seeking recognition for his autobiography; William H. Welch ("Popsy" Welch), one of the "Famous Four" in the well-known Sargent painting of four Johns Hopkins physicians, "dean of American medicine," vice president, president, and finally honorary president of the National Committee, whose enormous prestige opened many doors, both scientific and philanthropic, and whose hardheaded sense of first things first helped put the National Committee on a solid professional basis from the beginning; Henry Phipps, who gave the first major contribution to the new National Committee; William James, whose turning-point role has already been mentioned; William L. Russell, respected psychiatrist, teacher, and adviser; Adolf Meyer, first full-time professor of psychiatry in the United States, who recommended the name "Mental Hygiene" (a term first used in the title of a book in 1843) for the new movement, and who is described in the hundredth anniversary volume of the American Psychiatric Association as making "without any doubt . . . the most original and the greatest single contribution to American psychiatric literature;" and Thomas W. Salmon, sensitive and creative first medical director of the National Committee for Mental Hygiene, who in the words of his biographer, "built the structure and framed the program" through the early years of the National Committee, and whose name has come down to us today in the distinguished annual "Salmon Memorial Lectures" established in his honor.

III

"Tombs—But Not for the Quiet Dead"

Vignettes of Earlier Days

DESPITE OCCASIONAL instances of fine humanitarian ideals, the story of the care of the mentally ill for centuries back is an almost unrelieved horror tale to the point where at times one can hardly take in the words on the pages of history.

CRUELTY

All too vivid descriptions of torture and brutality spot the black records: fees charged to visitors who came to tease the "crazy" people — "a raree show;" "legg irons" and "madd-shirts;" windowless vaults six feet square; for sleeping, wet straw tossed on an iron frame; cold of such degree as to coat inside walls with frost; chains — forever chains — seventeen unrelieved years in at least one reported case; being bound to a tree in a public square and "striped till he waxed weary." One "pauper" was actually sold at auction and kept in an outhouse until his feet were frozen leaving only stumps; he was then chained lest he crawl away. These are but a few from among thousands of similar examples in the United States and all over the world.

Harsh treatment may arise out of cruelty, out of negligence, or out of ignorance, but the patient suffers just as much, whatever the motivation of his "cell-keepers." Endless maltreatment can be traced to misconceptions about the mentally ill — that they are insensitive to heat and cold, for instance. Or that shocks are good for them, such as being dropped through a trap door into a well of water. Or that they can be frightened back to normality, a mistake made even by some of the most humane of the early physicians who thought that because terror is a powerful force it "should be employed in the cure of madness." Among the "mild but terrifying" modes of treatment recommended were deprivation of food (on the principle that captured elephants are more tractable when starved to emaciation); and pulling a chair out from under a patient to convince him he was not made of glass.

These examples may sound as if they came out of past history impossible of repetition now. But they were not history in the early part of this century: they were common occurrences.

In 1913, for instance, on one of his field trips, Dr. Salmon saw conditions reminiscent of the worst horrors depicted throughout history: iron cages with sheet-metal backs and sides, stone floors, no light, no heat, no furniture except iron cots, forty-odd "inmates," in charge of a "yard man," never allowed outside their cages even when mortally ill. (Dr. Salmon wrote a poignant description entitled *The Insane in a County Poor Farm* which in 1917 appeared in Volume I, Number 1 of *Mental Hygiene,* and was later reprinted many times. And as late as World War II the men working in mental hospitals under the Civilian Public Service program of the Selective Service System accumulated eye-witness accounts of negligence and brutality second to none ever reported in past ages.)

DECENCY

But the idea of being decent to the mentally ill is not, of course, an invention of the twentieth century. Hippocrates in the fifth century B.C. showed remarkable scientific acumen in his recognition of mental disease not as a supernatural visitation but as an illness amenable to treatment, and if his insight had been more widely accepted, rationality — perhaps even kindness — might have been the rule instead of the exception for the last 2400 years. Others here and there throughout the centuries have spoken up on the side of sensitive understanding. A Greek physician in 124 B.C. berated his contemporaries for putting patients in dark quarters and prescribed sunlit rooms. The enigmatic Paracelsus in the sixteenth century said, "The insane and sick are our brothers. Let us give them treatment to cure them. . . ." Pinel "striking the chains" from the patients in the Paris Salpêtrière in 1795, and the progressive York Retreat operated by the Tukes in nineteenth century England, are well-known episodes.

PIONEERS

In our own country some splendid names splash brilliantly across the sordid pages. Some are scarcely known at all, such as Dr. George Zeller, who in 1902 at the Peoria State Hospital in Illinois was operating a completely "open-door" hospital — not partly open, but *open*, without bars or locks or "back wards," the kind of hospital barely beginning to be recognized today as the model and hope of the future. Other names — Benjamin Rush, Thomas Kirkbride, Dorothea Lynde Dix — have vivid stories behind them which can never be retold too often.

Benjamin Rush, signer of the Declaration of Independence, member of the Continental Congress, Surgeon General to the Continental Army during the Revolution, Treasurer of the United States Mint, passionate reformer, brilliant physician, was the first important American psychiatrist. After joining the staff of the Pennsylvania Hospital in 1783, he became the first American teacher to develop a comprehensive course of study in mental disease, and the first American physician to attempt an original systematization of the subject. His textbook published in 1812 remained the only American text until 1883. (One of his students for a short time was William Henry Harrison, who later became President of the United States: a psychiatrist in the White House — almost!) Rush's story is colorful to a degree, and parts of it are highly pertinent to our times.

Many years later, Thomas Story Kirkbride was another bright name on Pennsylvania Hospital's honorable roster of important contributors to medicine and psychiatry. When in 1841 the Pennsylvania Hospital opened a separate building to house the new "Department for the Insane," Kirkbride was appointed the first superintendent, a position he held for forty-three years; in fact, in the public mind his name became so identified with the hospital that it was known as "Kirkbride's." In 1844 he became one of the "original thirteen" founders of the Association of Medical Superintendents of American Institutions for the Insane, now the American Psychiatric Association. In

1851, at the request of the new organization, he submitted a list of twenty-six "Propositions," later elaborated into a famous document, *On the Construction and Organization of Hospitals for the Insane,* which not only became the standard text on the subject for the next thirty years, but even today, because of its emphasis on small hospitals built with wings radiating from a central administrative unit, is regarded as a marvel of good hospital planning.

Dorothea Lynde Dix, selfless, driving crusader, discovered her life's mission one winter day in 1841, when she visited the East Cambridge jail and saw the wretched cells where the insane were kept. From that day until her death in 1887, through hardship, ill health, and disappointment, her zeal never flagged. She was directly responsible for the building or enlarging of mental hospitals in twenty states and a dozen more in Europe. Her effective "memorials" to state legislatures were forerunners of the later appearances before legislatures and congressional hearings of more recent crusaders — Dr. Thomas W. Salmon in the early days of the National Committee for Mental Hygiene, Dr. George S. Stevenson throughout his long years of service with the Committee, and Dr. William C. Menninger in recent years.

In 1848 Dorothea Dix began her struggles to get Congress to pass a bill appropriating ten million acres of public land for the "indigent insane," comparable to the hundred million acres earlier given to the states for the purpose of extending higher education and from which the land grant colleges grew. Finally in 1851 both Houses of Congress simultaneously passed the bill, but President Pierce vetoed it, surely one of the most regrettable "if onlys" in American history. If only that bill had been passed, how different might have been the story of care of the mentally ill during the next hundred years in this country.

There were other admirable leaders in the fight for the mentally ill during the long period before the mental hygiene movement began to take shape, but space does not permit even a mention of their names. Their fine stories, however, and the dark stories too, have been supremely well told in *The Mentally Ill in America* by Albert Deutsch, another book of which it can be said, "It reads like fiction but it is not fiction."

Write the Vision Plain

The National Committee for Mental Hygiene and Some of Its Activities

GETTING A new reform movement under way was not easy, Clifford Beers soon found. For several years Beers was obliged to use his own funds — borrowed ones at that — for his organizing work. Then one day in November 1911 Dr. Welch received the following agreeable letter.

Dear Dr. Welch:

For some time past I have been thinking of what I could do towards ameliorating the condition of the insane in public and private institutions, and I shall be very glad, as mentioned to you this morning, if you will accept Fifty Thousand Dollars ($50,000) and appoint suitable parties to carry out such views as you may have on the subject.

I will send you a check whenever it is required.

Sincerely yours,
Henry Phipps

First Medical Director

Dr. Welch immediately recommended turning the money over to the National Committee for Mental Hygiene, and so at last the Committee was able to start active work with a paid staff. (A week later Mr. Phipps called to take Mr. Beers "motoring" and delicately offered him $5,000 for his personal use "to keep him from worrying" — which Mr. Beers applied toward paying off some of his debts!)

Early Planners

In their search for a medical director, Dr. William L. Russell introduced Mr. Beers to Dr. Thomas W. Salmon, of whom he thought highly. (In 1901, when Dr. Salmon was a young bacteriologist investigating an epidemic of diphtheria at Willard State Hospital in New York, he came under the tutelage of Dr. Russell, and thus became one of those psychiatrists who, in the early days, got their psychiatry "by exposure," luckily, in this case, exposure to the kindly and gifted Dr. Russell.) At the time of the introduction, Dr. Salmon was on loan to the Public Health Service from the New York State Board of Alienists. He had been doing some statistical work developing charts which showed, among other things, that the proportion of foreign born in mental hospitals was twice that of the foreign born in the general population (studies which were to prove useful later at the National Committee). Both the Public Health Service and the Board in Lunacy agreed to release Dr. Salmon and he started to work for the National Committee in 1912. Mr. Beers was secretary of the Committee, a position he retained until a few years before his death in 1943.

With Beers and Salmon at the head ("a great team") and

Welch, Meyer, and Russell, soon joined by Frankwood Williams, who later became second medical director, the early planners included some of the most important names in psychiatry and related fields, not only of that day but of this. Most of them are now dead, and our debt to all of them is very great.

As part of their conception for the National Committee, the planners believed that it should initiate important activities, carry them along if there were no other organization to do so, shift responsibility to an appropriate group if one existed, or if not, create one, meanwhile co-operating and collaborating with other organizations which had relevant goals, and that has been the way the national body has functioned during most of its fifty years.

EARLY ACTIVITIES

After the staff had started to work in 1912, the first official business of the Committee was the adoption of a resolution urging Congress to provide for adequate mental examination of immigrants. This grew in part out of Dr. Salmon's earlier experience when he had been in the Public Health Service assigned to Ellis Island. At that time, the United States was experiencing one of the greatest waves of immigration any country has ever known. In 1907, more than 1,000,000 people entered the port of New York, and medical officers were examining as many as 5,000 immigrants a day. The plight of mentally ill aliens was tragic. They were deported, with all the disappointment that entailed, but worse, many of them never reached home again and relatives were unable to find out what had happened to them.

For some time prior to his National Committee appointment, Dr. Salmon had been working with the State Charities Aid Association in New York trying to have the Immigration Act changed in such a way as to place more responsibility on the steamship companies for returning insane aliens, and on the Public Health Service for their proper care on these shores. Finally with the help of the National Committee, some of the worst of the abuses were corrected, and the entire system of reception and examination was revamped.

As the new organization got under way, the small staff had to do everything at once. They prepared lists of psychiatrists and of public and private mental institutions, and a bibliography on nervous and mental diseases, none of which had ever existed before. They started collecting and analyzing laws pertaining to the mentally ill and making them available to legislative bodies and civic groups. And they started a program of public education, which included an exhibit, and the preparation of four pamphlets, of which they distributed 91,000 copies that first working year — not a bad distribution figure for those days.

STATISTICS

One of the staff's biggest jobs was to start getting the facts concerning the mentally ill in institutions. They tried to develop a method of uniform reporting about patients in institutions but immediately ran into the problem of nomenclature because there was as yet no agreement among psychiatrists and institutions about the classification of mental disorders. Beginning in 1914, the National Committee cooperated with the American Medico-Psychological Association (since 1921 the American Psychiatric Association) and the American Association for the Study of the Feebleminded (now the American Association on Mental Deficiency) in the development of standard nomenclature approved by all three organizations in 1918.

They also cooperated with those same two groups and

with appropriate federal agencies, especially the Public Health Service and the Department of Commerce and Labor, in developing uniform reporting and assigning responsibility for collecting adequate statistics on mental patients. Beginning in 1917, the National Committee published annual statistical reports, a responsibility it continued to carry until 1923, when an enumeration of patients in mental institutions was for the first time included in the decennial nation-wide census, and the federal Bureau of the Census took over full responsibility for reporting statistics on mental patients.

SURVEYS

But perhaps the Committee's most nearly unique job and most important contribution lay in the staff's surveys of institutions for the mentally ill, mentally defective, and epileptic. Clifford Beers had told them what they would find — and they found it! The inspections extended beyond institutions intended for the mentally ill to other institutions in which they were also kept, such as jails, county poor farms, almshouses, old people's homes and orphan asylums. (At that time in more than half the states the mentally ill were regularly put in jails and almshouses.)

After each survey, which was made only at the request of the institution or some other responsible organization, the staff would try to lay the facts before appropriate legislative bodies and civic groups. Following one of Dr. Salmon's surveys in North Carolina, when he brought the facts to the attention of the governor and the legislature, so many improvements were effected so fast that Dr. Salmon wrote an article describing the experience entitled *Fifty Years Progress in Forty Days.* Dr Salmon devoted the major portion of his time to these surveys during his first several years with the Committee, and then Dr. Williams in his turn. "No other activity of the National Committee has brought results so important in proportion to the money expended," it has been said of these early surveys.

For a quarter of a century the name most closely associated with the hospital surveys was Samuel W. Hamilton, M.D., known to mental hospital administrators everywhere. Dr. Hamilton first assisted the National Committee with its surveys in 1917. In 1924 he was appointed director of the National Committee's new Division on Hospital Services. In 1936 he became the executive of the Mental Hospital Survey Committee, which was sponsored by eight professional and health organizations including the National Committee for Mental Hygiene, the American Psychiatric Association, and the Public Health Service, and later continued to direct the work after it was taken over by the Public Health Service in 1939.

(To bring the story of hospital surveys up to date: Further refinements of the survey idea were added by the American Psychiatric Association in 1948, when it established an inspection and rating system for mental hospitals, the Central Inspection Board. Armed with official standards, the Central Inspection Board in effect handed the American people a professional yardstick with which they could for the first time evaluate the adequacy of their hospitals. In 1958, the Joint Commission on Accreditation of Hospitals began to inspect and rate mental as well as general hospitals, and it was agreed that the Central Inspection Board's inspection and rating functions would terminate in 1961, although the American Psychiatric Association would continue to provide consultation to the hospitals and to state governments.)

RECRUITMENT AND TRAINING

Another major problem of the early period, and another that has a familiar ring today, was the matter of professional personnel: recruiting and training psychiatrists and other key personnel who dealt directly with the mentally ill.

The urgency of the need for finding adequate personnel and for providing the necessary funds to train them and *keep* them has been repeatedly and forcefully stated throughout the years. As early as World War I, Dr. Salmon warned that the contemplated new veterans' hospitals would become "sepulchers of science" unless funds were forthcoming to staff them properly. Dr. George Preston described the problem graphically when he said, "No building ever cured a patient. Patients can be cured only by trained people. They can be cured at home or in tents, or on farms, or crowded wards, if there are enough trained people to spend enough time with each patient." Dr. Karl Menninger said the same thing in his often-quoted statement: "Many patients will get well in a barn if you give them the right doctors and the right treatment. We don't *want* them to live in barns, but staff and treatment must come first." His brother, Dr. William Menninger, epitomized this theme in the phrase "Brains before Bricks," which he has used as the title of many of his talks before state legislatures, to convey the idea that if citizens (taxpayers) will place enough emphasis on buying brains, they will not have to buy so many bricks.

In the early years of the National Committee, only a few medical schools had departments of psychiatry, and the work which went into the development of training was one of the factors which helped to provide a good foundation for the entire movement. Some of the institutions which were among the first to provide good psychiatric training were the Boston Psychopathic Hospital, Henry Phipps Psychiatric Clinic, Pennsylvania Hospital, and Colorado Psychopathic Hospital — with financial assistance from the Commonwealth Fund and Rockefeller Foundation. (Later the Commonwealth Fund supported extensive programs in several medical schools to further the development of psychiatric teaching for all medical students.)

From the inception of the National Committee, members of the staff had done what they could about professional training as they went about their business. It was not until 1923, however, that the Committee was able to undertake a more systematic effort in support of training. At that time, the Commonwealth Fund and the Rockefeller Foundation started a series of grants for training fellowships, the awards to be made through the National Committee and the training carried out under its supervision. The Committee continued to administer a fellowship program until the late 1940's when it was turned over to the American Association of Psychiatric Clinics for Children. In recent years, fellowship funds have been available through the National Institute of Mental Health.

CERTIFICATION

By 1931 the need for certification of psychiatrists, a matter closely related to psychiatric training, had become urgent. The National Committee created a Division of Psychiatric Education (Franklin G. Ebaugh, M.D., director) and collaborated with the American Psychiatric Association in studying medical school curricula and promoting the improvement of training. In 1934 the APA in cooperation with the National Committee, the American Neurological Association, and the American Medical Association, created the American Board of Psychiatry and Neurology which examines candidates for certification. Some of the psychiatrists who were trained before 1919 were certified under the "grandfather clause" — meaning that they were approved on record. Today most younger men in psychiatry consider it desirable to achieve Board certification if they can (the examinations are exceedingly difficult) in order to be regarded as qualified by their peers.

PROFESSIONAL ASSOCIATIONS

In addition to having a hand in creating the Central Inspection Board and the American Board of Psychiatry and Neurology, the National Committee offered hospitality to the American Psychiatric Association, to the American Orthopsychiatric Association, the American Association of Psychiatric Social Workers, and the American Association of Psychiatric Clinics for Children, all of which had their first quarters in the offices of the Committee.

From its inception the National Committee worked closely with the American Psychiatric Association, and it would be hard to count the number of projects on which they collaborated. The American Psychiatric Association has bestowed its highest honor, the presidency of the Association, on two of the four medical directors of the National Committee: Thomas W. Salmon, M.D., the first medical director, and George S. Stevenson, M.D., the fourth. The following presidents of the Association have been members of the staff, consultants, trustees, or officers, of the National Committee or its successor, the National Association for Mental Health:

Kenneth E. Appel, M.D.

Leo H. Bartemeier, M.D.

Earl D. Bond, M.D.

Karl M. Bowman, M.D.

Francis J. Braceland, M.D.

Robert Felix, M.D.

Samuel W. Hamilton, M.D.

C. Floyd Haviland, M.D.

William Malamud, M.D.

William C. Menninger, M.D.

Adolf Meyer, M.D.

Winfred Overholser, M.D.

William L. Russell, M.D.

Thomas W. Salmon, M.D.

George S. Stevenson, M.D.

Edward A. Strecker, M.D.

William Alanson White, M.D.

John C. Whitehorn, M.D.

FOUNDATIONS

Good works go farther with funds behind them and the mental health movement has had some loyal friends both among individuals and foundations. In the annals of the National Committee, two foundation names occur over and over and over again: the Rockefeller Foundation and the Commonwealth Fund. Much of their support was behind the scenes and is not well known to the public. Their contributions both in money and leadership have been generous.

Other foundations which have made significant contributions include the Carnegie Corporation, Field Foundation, Grant Foundation, Ittleson Family Foundation, Josiah Macy, Jr. Foundation, Milbank Memorial Fund, New York Foundation, Rockefeller Brothers Fund, and Julius Rosenwald Fund. Another loyal financial backer for many years, not a foundation but operating in the same manner through grants-in-aid, is the Supreme Council, Thirty-Third Degree, Ancient Accepted Scottish Rite, Northern Masonic Jurisdiction, U.S.A., which since 1934 has financed a program of research in schizophrenia, administered by the National Committee, and now by the National Association for Mental Health. The total contributions of the Scottish Rite Masons now approximate one and one-half million dollars. Their support began long before the necessity for research in schizophrenia had gained any popular acceptance to speak of, and they have earned the gratitude of the mental health movement for their foresight and their loyalty.

V

The Cinderella Story

Psychiatry Takes Its Proper Place

THE EXPRESSION "psychiatry as the Cinderella of medicine"
— heard often at one time although rarely now — originated with an amusing satire Dr. Salmon wrote in 1920
about a young girl who lived with her two favorite sisters,
Medicine and Surgery, and was wooed by Prince Public
Favor who finally recognized her by her dainty Sam
Browne belt embroidered "Practical Usefulness." The
metaphor aptly described the long period during which
psychiatry was primarily institutional, not yet accorded its
present acceptance (for instance, when Dr. Salmon was
in the Public Health Service psychiatrists received the
same pay as policemen), with its vast potential still unrecognized.

EMERGENCE

Historians of psychiatry date its emergence from institutional isolation variously from 1900 to 1914, but they all agree that up until then psychiatry *had* been isolated and that it *did* emerge. Many forces entered into bringing about the emergence. Among them: the growing population of the United States with correspondingly greater numbers of the mentally ill; the turn of the century as a period of social reform, and increasing public acceptance of social responsibility; the growth of the scientific method and important new medical discoveries; improved medical schools resulting in better medical and psychiatric training; the new ideas of the period, especially the concept of psychogenesis; and, not least, the recognition of psychiatry's "practical usefulness."

(Speaking of "emergence," the Original Thirteen founders of the American Psychiatric Association would assuredly concur that their profession had emerged — but definitely — if they were to step into an annual meeting of the Association nowadays, with attendance ranging as high as 4,000 people; then they might visit the Washington office in its own building, the New York office, and several of the branch offices established for special projects in other parts of the country. Membership in the Association which was under 500 in 1908 has almost doubled in every decade but one since then, and now exceeds 11,000.)

PSYCHOPATHIC HOSPITALS

Interestingly enough, psychopathic hospitals, which saw their greatest growth during the first quarter of the twentieth century and which have played a lively role in therapy and research for the last fifty years, reflected all the social forces described above and provided the setting for some of the most important contributions of the emerging psychiatry. (The term "psychopathic hospitals" was used in order to differentiate them from the custodial "insane asylums" of the period. The nearest equivalent today is the more general term "psychiatric hospitals.")

From the beginning, psychopathic hospitals have fulfilled a variety of functions: They are clearing houses for cases where diagnosis or disposition is uncertain; they give first care to patients before commitment; they provide short, intensive therapy for incipient cases; they train medical and psychiatric personnel; they are centers for outpatient services; and they are research centers.

Historically, psychopathic hospitals grew out of urgent community needs. Even before 1900, public indignation was being repeatedly aroused by incidents in which a mentally ill or mentally defective person would be arrested and beaten by the police and then thrown into the workhouse, or even sent to a penitentiary before his mental condition was recognized. Some cities attempted to cope with the problem by establishing wards for temporary detention, such as the "Insane Pavilion" at Bellevue Hospital in New York City, constructed in 1879, and "Pavilion F" at the Albany Hospital, opened in 1902, the first psychopathic ward in a general hospital. Though not having a psychopathic ward, the Pennsylvania Hospital should be mentioned in this context because it was the first general hospital to receive mental patients, from the time it was built in 1752, and it provided outpatient services as early as 1885. The Henry Phipps Clinic at Johns Hopkins Hospital, beginning in 1913, was another early forerunner with many of the features of a psychopathic hospital. And two other notable pioneers were mentioned in the first chapter: The State Psychopathic Hospital at the University of Michigan, which opened in 1907 after several years of preliminary experimentation with psychopathic wards, was the first psychopathic hospital in the United States; and the Boston Psychopathic Hospital in 1912 was the first one connected with a state hospital system, and incidentally the first to open an outpatient clinic for children (not to be confused, however, with the first child guidance clinics which were on a different pattern).

PSYCHOGENESIS

Perhaps the most exciting of the new ideas which were to see rapid development during the decade within which this history begins was the evolution of the idea of psychogenesis — the concept that mental illness and other symptoms are produced by mental and emotional factors as opposed to organic ones. Up to then psychiatry had been almost exclusively organic and neurological. A writer in the *Journal of Insanity* in 1905 remarked that it took daring at that stage of neurological research to advance the view "that there are diseases of function as well as of organs." Under the influence of Bleuler, Freud, and Jung in Europe and Adolf Meyer, William Alanson White, and Smith Ely Jelliffe in this country, psychogenic concepts began to appear extensively in the psychiatric literature. This was the beginning of a long period — stretching well into the 1940's — when there was so much stress on the role of environment in mental disorder that the organicists took a certain amount of abuse. In the last decade or so the pendulum has swung well back and interest in searching out organic factors is again keen. Nevertheless, such has been the acceptance of psychogenic concepts as to make it improbable that science will ever again negate their significance. Indeed the contribution of psychogenesis not only to the treatment of mental illness but also to the understanding of normal behavior is so great as to be utterly incalculable. ·

FADS

Psychiatry has not been without its fads and exaggerations now and then, and some of them got a good deal of publicity during the 1920's, such as the notion that psychoses were caused by focal infections and could be cured by vitamins or thyroidectomy. Some of these were reminiscent of the "cult of curability" a century earlier (graphically described by Albert Deutsch in *The Mentally Ill in America*) when institutions vied with each other as to which could report the highest percentage of cures, and claims ran as high as 100 per cent. (This was not too difficult to achieve when each discharge was by definition regarded as a cure. Thus a patient discharged 48 times went down in the record as 48 cures — and that actually happened; in another instance three patients admitted 118 times were reported cured 102 times.) Matters did not get quite as far out of hand as that during the 1920's but there was a good deal of nonsense and also the beginning of some of the overselling and false expectations which have plagued psychiatry ever since.

EARLY BREAKTHROUGHS

A more important development of this period (the first quarter century) was the rapid growth of therapy and research. Adolf Meyer, beginning in 1902 at the New York State Pathological Institute on Ward's Island (before he went to Johns Hopkins and developed his theories of psychobiology), is usually credited with having brought pathological research in psychiatry "out of the dead house" and into the laboratory. Practically all historians of psychiatry agree, however, that the first big breakthrough in psychiatric research was the discovery in 1913 that the syphilis spirochete causes paresis (or, as it was often called then, "general paralysis of the insane"). That was followed in 1917 by the discovery of the efficacy of fever treatment for paresis, and a short time later by the use of malaria, which was introduced to this country by White at St. Elizabeths Hospital in Washington, D.C., in 1922.

Here then, in a short four year span, for the first time in the history of psychiatry, both the etiology of an important mental disorder and a specific treatment for it had been pinned down. At that time the life expectancy of paretics was three to five years after hospitalization, and paresis accounted for approximately 10 per cent of the admissions to mental hospitals. (In recent years, largely due to penicillin, this has dropped to about 2 per cent.) Incidentally, these two discoveries — the syphilis spirochete as a cause and malaria as a cure — represented the partnership of pathological and clinical research so often found in medicine. Pathological research (laboratories, microscopes, test tubes) identified the cause; clinical observation ("clinical" by derivation pertaining to "bedside" and therefore to doctors treating patients) discovered the cure.

"NEW" THERAPIES

The next big excitement over potential "cures" came in 1933, with the discovery of insulin shock treatment by Sakel in Vienna, followed shortly by metrazol, both of which were introduced to the United States about 1936, and then by electric convulsive shock therapy in 1938. Evidence of the amount of excitement generated is seen in the fact that between 1933 and 1941 more than 1,000 articles on metrazol appeared in the literature. As it turned out later, claims were overrated. Despite this, however, the introduction of shock therapy provided tremendous stimulus for research both in first class hospitals and in back-water custodial institutions which had theretofore regarded research as completely outside their scope.

Psychosurgery (operation on the intact brain) — another big excitement during that period — was first carried out on mental patients in Portugal in 1933 and like the various shock therapies has become a subject for a certain amount of controversy within the profession as to circumstances under which it is indicated and claims for efficacy.

DRUGS

The next dramatic breakthrough came in the early 1950's with the sudden appearance of the tranquilizing drugs. For a time the magic words chlorpromazine and reserpine were on every tongue — but soon there were so many new drugs the tongue began to trip. Claims of "cures" were once more wildly optimistic, and also once again it soon became necessary to tone them down and admit that, although tranquilizers made mental patients more manageable and more amenable to psychotherapy, they were not in themselves "cures."

Even though the first extravagant hopes were not borne out in full, tranquilizers nevertheless proved far more effective than the shock therapies and have been one of the factors responsible for the larger numbers of discharges from mental hospitals within the past decade.

BASIC RESEARCH

More technical and less publicized than drug therapy is the great range of steady plodding research into causes that goes on year after year in countless laboratories and clinics. Here too, drugs are playing a dramatic role — not drugs for therapy, but those which induce states resembling psychoses (especially schizophrenia) in normal people — on the theory that the study of simulated psychoses may lead to the understanding of true psychoses. Among the drugs being studied are lysergic acid diethylamide (LSD), mescaline, and some of the little known drugs used for centuries by peoples in other cultures to bring about temporary changes in consciousness. (Researchers have not yet reached semantic agreement as to whether such drugs are to be called hallucinogens, psychedelics, psychotomimetics, psychodysleptics or any of several other polysyllabic neologisms.)

Research in organic factors is holding out the hope of eventually being able to isolate an enzyme responsible for precipitating psychosis. Significant research into psychic factors is, of course, also being carried on, and many investigators predict that when the causes of schizophrenia are finally isolated, they will prove to be a combination of organic and psychic factors. But all this is history in the making with the crucial answers still in the future.

VI

"We Must Reach Them Earlier"

Child Guidance Clinics,
Residential Treatment,
and Child Psychiatry

THE CHILD guidance clinic movement started with people who were concerned about juvenile delinquency. In those days, even as now, juvenile delinquency was a grave problem, and dreadful things were being done to children in the name of punishment. (One judge in one year sentenced sixty-five children to jail and forty others to a chain gang.) In 1920 the new Commonwealth Fund (established in 1918) sought the advice of the National Committee for Mental Hygiene about the Fund's program. Dr.

Salmon cited the pioneer work of Dr. William Healy in Chicago. At a conference at Lakewood, N.J., in 1921 under the auspices of the Commonwealth Fund and the National Committee, the Commonwealth Fund agreed to finance a five-year program on the "prevention of juvenile delinquency" which was to be administered by the National Committee. The idea was to extend Dr. Healy's type of work by establishing similar clinics in other cities.

FIRST CLINIC

As has been mentioned, Dr. Healy had started his Juvenile Psychopathic Institute in 1909, financed for the first five years by Mrs. W. F. Dummer of Chicago — (a bow to Mrs. Dummer for her support of this history-making project.) In 1917 Dr. Healy and his gifted psychologist associate, Dr. Augusta Bronner (later Mrs. William Healy) were invited to go to Boston to head the new Judge Baker Foundation (now the Judge Baker Guidance Center) which was to become the prototype of all child guidance clinics. (When Dr. Healy left Chicago, Dr. Herman Adler took over his work and developed the Institute of Juvenile Research, which for many years continued to be one of the important pioneering institutions.)

CLINIC TEAM

The genius of the early child guidance clinics lay in their "team" concept: psychiatrists, psychiatric social workers, and clinical psychologists working together, each carrying those clinical responsibilities for which he was prepared by his special training, pooling their findings on each case, and then arriving at a plan of treatment. The usual pattern of the early clinics was that the psychiatric social worker obtained the developmental and social history and worked with parents, schools, and social agencies;

the psychologist assessed the child's mental abilities; and the psychiatrist, who was usually the clinic administrator, conducted the physical and psychiatric examination of the child and the psychotherapy. Later, there were many modifications in that pattern but not in the basic team idea.

DEMONSTRATION CLINICS

As soon as the National Committee's new Division on the Prevention of Delinquency was established in 1922, it began to send out psychiatric field service teams to organize clinics in different cities. (The term "child guidance clinic" was coined that year.) The teams quickly learned two important lessons: that if a child guidance clinic is to succeed, it must have the backing of a number of concerned community organizations; and that in order to prevent delinquency, it is essential to reach a child long before he arrives at the juvenile court stage — a concept which quickly came to pervade all work with problem children.

Because of the stress on juvenile delinquency, the first clinics were thought of as adjuncts to juvenile courts and were so offered to the community. The first of the Commonwealth Fund demonstration clinics was in St. Louis, where it was connected with the Juvenile Court, but it also had the backing of the community and so became established on a permanent basis. The second one, in Norfolk, Virginia, lacked essential community support and was the only one in the series which failed. The third one, in Dallas, Texas, was placed on a broader basis from the beginning and was tied to the schools and social agencies. The others in the demonstration series were established in Minneapolis and St. Paul (jointly at the University of Minnesota), Los Angeles, Cleveland, and Philadelphia, in that order.

In 1927, when the Commonwealth Fund demonstration period ended, the National Committee broadened its concept of the function of child guidance clinics and established a Division on Community Clinics with George S. Stevenson, M.D., as director of the Division (a position he retained until 1939 when he was appointed medical director of the Committee). The Division served as a clearing house and advisory service for child guidance clinics, and it administered the fellowship training program which had been established earlier by the Commonwealth Fund for the training of psychiatrists, clinical psychologists, and psychiatric social workers preparing for child guidance clinic work. From the late 1920's on, the number of child guidance clinics increased rapidly. During the next five years, after the close of the demonstration period, 27 cities established full-time child guidance clinics and several hundred set up some kind of part-time service.

Many of the early clinics became important training centers for child guidance clinic personnel, and many of the directors became important leaders in child psychiatry. It is regrettable that space does not permit recording their names here.

In the same year that the demonstration clinic program was being planned (1921), the Commonwealth Fund also gave funds to the New York School of Social Work to establish a Bureau of Children's Guidance, headed by Bernard Glueck, M.D., and Marion E. Kenworthy, M.D. (In 1957, the Marion E. Kenworthy endowed Chair of Psychiatry was established at the New York School of Social Work, Columbia University.) Another notable clinic supported by the Commonwealth Fund was the distinguished Institute for Child Guidance, of which Lawson G. Lowrey, M.D., was the executive director, and David M. Levy, M.D., the chief of staff. In its short but brilliant career, lasting from 1927 to 1933, that clinic trained an impressive number of psychiatrists, psychiatric social workers, and clinical psychologists.

As with many other developments touched on so briefly in this short history, it would take a full book to do justice to an evaluation of the child guidance clinic movement in America. Suffice it to say that child guidance clinics have contributed significantly to psychiatric therapy, to research, to psychiatric training, to the training of other professions, to public education in mental health — especially parent education — and to the concept of community responsibility for health and welfare.

ORTHOPSYCHIATRY

Two important professional organizations — the American Orthopsychiatric Association and the American Association of Psychiatric Clinics for Children — developed directly out of the child guidance clinic movement. The American Orthopsychiatric Association was organized in 1924 by the same kind of group that created the American Psychiatric Association and the National Committee — a small knot of people with a common vital interest, in this case preventive psychiatry. It started with a letter signed by Dr. Karl Menninger and sent to twenty-six psychiatrists in December 1923 soliciting their participation in forming a new organization of "representatives of the neuropsychiatric or medical view of crime." They chose the prefix "ortho" (derived from the Greek, meaning straighten) because they thought it conveyed the idea with which they were concerned: "straightmindedness," or more literally "straightness of spirit." (They would have preferred "orthopsychics" but they feared misinterpretation.)

Following some preliminary discussions, the founding meeting was held on January 13, 1924 at the Institute for

Juvenile Research in Chicago, attended by Herman M. Adler, V. V. Anderson, Arnold Jacoby, David M. Levy, and George S. Stevenson — all psychiatrists — and a few members of the staff of the Institute. William Healy was the first president. Volume I, number 1 of the *American Journal of Orthopsychiatry* appeared in October 1930 with Lawson G. Lowrey, M.D. as editor, a position he retained for almost 20 years, during which period he built up the journal to its present respected status as spokesman for preventive psychiatry.

From the beginning the American Orthopsychiatric Association has been multiprofessional. Members are psychiatrists, psychologists, and psychiatric social workers, with a sprinkling of other professionals with similar interests. Membership requirements are rigid. A member must, among other things, have worked in a clinic regularly utilizing the coordinated services of psychiatrists, clinical psychologists, and psychiatric social workers. The organization has grown from a few score in the 1920's to several hundred in the 1940's, and over 1,600 now, with attendance at meetings sometimes exceeding 5,000. The Association has had a tremendous influence on all clinical work.

The American Association of Psychiatric Clinics for Children, a relative newcomer — having been established in 1948 — is the standard-setting agency for child guidance clinics. Its members are not individuals but clinics, and it is little known outside the child guidance clinic field. It performs essential functions comparable to certification in establishing standards for training of clinic personnel and for the quality of clinical services.

Residential Treatment

The development of inpatient treatment of mentally ill children has lagged far behind child guidance clinics and there are still only a handful of facilities in the country. This means that mentally ill children if hospitalized must often be placed in wards with adults; or if they are still at home their parents are usually at their wits' ends trying first one resource and then another, with the child rarely getting the treatment he needs.

Historically, the first impetus for providing some sort of inpatient services for mentally ill children occurred in the early 1920's when there was a wave of postencephalitic behavior disorders which presented extraordinarily difficult problems in diagnosis and care and for a while had the psychiatric world sorely puzzled. The Franklin School in Philadelphia was the first institution established to treat these children. (The director was Earl D. Bond, M.D., whose name appears a number of times in this account.)

In 1930, two state mental hospitals — Allentown in Pennsylvania and Rockland in New York — created children's units, the first of their kind. Other pioneering firsts in the 1930's were the Hawthorne-Cedar Knolls School of the Jewish Board of Guardians in New York, the Emma Pendleton Bradley Home in Providence, and the Ryther Children's Center in Seattle. The first residential center to stress research, to the point of including the word in its title, was the Henry Ittleson Center for Child Research, opened in New York in 1953.

Several forces have entered into the development of residential treatment centers: The first one, chronologically, was the discovery that there are many children who cannot be treated in outpatient services, and for whom existing child-caring institutions are inadequate. A second force was the growing awareness of how many mentally ill children there are. Although it is not yet possible to prove the point conclusively, informed opinion inclines toward the belief that the number of such children is increasing.

Another force was the changing concept of what constitutes good care for normal children who must be cared for outside their own homes — that is, the conviction that foster care in a private family is better for a child than congregate care, and the resulting decrease in the numbers of institutions for congregate care in the United States. Consequently, many institutions for dependent children are now being converted into residential treatment centers on the principle that although institutional care is not good for normal children, it may be the treatment of choice for disturbed children. Moreover, there has been an increasing number of disturbed children in foster care, thereby necessitating the establishment of institutions to care for those whose emotional disorders are such as to make it impossible for them to adjust in a foster home.

A final force accounting for the development of residential treatment centers has been the demonstration of the value of "milieu therapy" in psychiatric institutions, where clinical services are, in effect, built-in. In such institutions, the child experiences a tolerance for behavior which would be unacceptable elsewhere, along with a carefully planned daily regime of routines, control, and protection — all of which is integrated into the "total push" which helps him improve. (And indeed the same principles also apply to the institutional care of mentally ill adults.)

In the early days of first enthusiasm about child guidance clinics, more than a few were established in communities which had not as yet built the fundamental services for children, such as a good family agency, a children's agency providing foster care services, an understanding juvenile court, and recreation facilities; and the same thing has been happening with respect to residential centers. All these community services must come before either a clinic or a residential center can function constructively. The Child Welfare League of America, which is the standard-setting agency in the child care field, takes the stand that it will not recommend any new residential center in a community if basic child care services are still lacking, or if that community still has substandard institutions which "turn out problem children faster than any residential service can possibly adjust them."

Among the difficulties experienced by residential centers are inordinately high costs, finding and keeping adequate staff (the ratio of staff to patients must necessarily be high), and the whole range of complications around community support and integration with other community agencies. Partly because of all these difficulties, some centers are now experimenting with new patterns of day care which look promising for the future. The National Organization for Mentally Ill Children is one of the agencies striving to expand day care facilities in local communities throughout the country.

CHILD PSYCHIATRY

The biggest single problem in providing good psychiatric care for children — bigger even than finding the money — is finding well-trained personnel. Although the problem of personnel scarcity cuts across all psychiatry and all the related professions, it is especially acute in child psychiatry. Something seems to have happened to child psychiatry. It has not fulfilled the promise of its youth in the 1920's. In those days, when the demand for child psychiatrists so greatly exceeded the supply, the hope was constantly being expressed that "in another ten years" training would "catch up." But it has not. Now, thirty-five years later, the scarcity is just as acute.

The painful fact is that astonishingly few well-trained child psychiatrists are being turned out — fewer than fifty a year — and there are not a hundred *"qualified"* child psychiatrists in the United States. Although all medical schools now have departments of psychiatry and most of them give some work in child psychiatry, few have developed major programs in child psychiatry and only one has an endowed chair — the Blanche F. Ittleson Chair of Child Psychiatry in the Medical School at Washington University in St. Louis, established in 1956 with E. James Anthony, M.D., formerly of Maudsley Hospital, London, appointed in 1958 as the first incumbent. (Blanche F. Ittleson is Mrs. Henry Ittleson, to whom this book is dedicated.)

The situation with respect to the small number of child psychiatrists is the more surprising because the importance of child psychiatry has been very great, and continues to be. (This fact was officially attested in 1959 when the American Board of Psychiatry and Neurology gave child psychiatry the status of a specialty and established certification for child psychiatrists.) The insights of child psychiatry have permeated the entire field of psychiatry, as well as related fields, and indeed all the helping professions and all child care. But as to why more young psychiatrists do not choose child psychiatry, and why more than the expected number leave the children's field after having been trained, speculation is rife but answers are not definitive.

VII

Wanted: A Word

The Care of the Mentally Retarded

IT IS A curious fact that there is no proper word for the mentally retarded in institutions. They are quite commonly called "children," but of course most of them are adults. "Patient" does not seem right because although they are "under care" they are not ill. "Inmate" has an undesirable prison connotation. "Retardate" is a recent neologism, but whether it will take hold is impossible to predict. Furthermore, there is no satisfactory noun to go with the modifiers "mentally retarded" and "mentally deficient." So one ends up using the phrase *"the* mentally retarded" — an abstraction — which the mentally retarded are not. Surely there must be a lesson for us in this anomaly if we have the wisdom to read it.

EARLY ATTITUDES

Although by and large the mentally retarded have not been submitted to anything like as much cruelty as have the mentally ill, nevertheless they have suffered more than their share of neglect. An attitude of centuries' standing was put into words by a Connecticut legislative committee in 1856 when it reported that it had found "a settled conviction of the large majority of citizens of the commonwealth that idiots were a class so utterly hopeless that it was a waste of time even to collect any statistics concerning them." Such a forthright statement could scarcely get by today, but the attitude it expresses is not as rare as one might wish.

At the turn of the century, when this account begins, "idiot" was still the generic term for mentally defective. An institution for them, now preferably called either "school" or "hospital and school," was then called an "asylum for idiots," sometimes with the addition "and feeble-minded." The present Walter E. Fernald State School in Massachusetts was then the Massachusetts School for Idiotic and Feeble Minded Youth. And the Association of Medical Officers of American Institutions for Idiots and Feeble Minded Persons had only recently, in 1906, changed its name to the American Association on Mental Deficiency.

EARLY LEADERSHIP

At about the time the National Committee for Mental Hygiene started to work in 1912, concerned citizen groups were waking up both to the numbers of mentally deficient — which was a shock — and to the lack of community facilities. In New York City the State Charities Aid Association was in the process of uncovering a bad local situation with overcrowding in institutions and a long waiting list (3,000), and also an outright scandal due to the system of recruiting alcoholics and "itinerant tramps" from the workhouses and municipal lodgings as caretakers in the city's institution for the feeble minded (a system, by the way, then painfully prevalent throughout the country in recruiting "guards" and "keepers" for mental patients). The National Committee jumped into that local fight but it was several years before adequate reforms were brought about.

From the beginning, the National Committee had included institutions for the mentally defective along with those for the mentally ill in its surveys, and had discovered many of the same wretched conditions. In Kentucky in 1916, for instance, the National Committee found that the state was still operating under a "Pauper-Idiot Law" dating from 1793. From 1915 on, Dr. Walter E. Fernald, one of the great leaders in the field, was active with the National Committee in its subcommittee on mental deficiency, and in 1917 the National Committee established a Division on Mental Deficiency. With support from the Rockefeller Foundation, the institution surveys were extended, and as a result institutions for the mentally defective were enlarged and improved in many states.

Another historically important figure in the struggle to improve the lot of the mentally defective in that period was Dr. Henry H. Goddard of the Training School at Vineland, N.J. In 1908, as previously mentioned, Dr. Goddard had introduced the Binet-Simon mental tests to this country, and in 1910 he presented his classification of three levels of feeble-mindedness — idiot, imbecile, and moron — which is still in use today.

EUGENICS

A phenomenon of the early 1900's was the rising "eugenic alarm." Back in the middle 1800's, Seguin of France, an earlier protagonist for the mentally deficient, had preached a gospel of sympathy for them. But by the early 1900's, based on what later proved to be more fiction than truth and embellished by dramatic but apocryphal tales of families such as the Jukes and the Kallikaks, the mentally defective rather suddenly began to be regarded as a dire threat even to civilization itself. Claims were fantastically exaggerated. "Mental deficiency, mother of crime, pauperism, and degeneracy" was a typical statement of the period. "A parasitic predatory class . . . invariably immoral . . . carriers of venereal disease . . . potential criminals . . . ," and so forth. (This was 1915.)

STERILIZATION

The excitement aroused by pseudoscientific reports of the menace of the feeble-minded led to drastic legislation. Indiana was the first state (1907) to pass a law for the compulsory sterilization of "confirmed criminals, idiots, imbeciles and rapists." Other states followed with similar statutes. Some of these were later repealed as violating the "due process of law" clause of the fourteenth amendment if they permitted sterilization for the purpose of punishment, although in 1927 the constitutionality of sterilization for eugenic reasons was upheld by the United States Supreme Court. In 1930, selective sterilization was endorsed by the American Association for the Study of the Feeble-Minded and by the White House Conference on Children. The extremes of ignorance back of some of the measures, however, are represented by one piece of state legislation introduced in 1929, which would have permitted sterilization for "highway robbery, bombing and chicken stealing."

By the middle 1930's, more than half the states had eugenic sterilization laws on their books, but in only a few states were they operative. Sterilization is now thought to be decreasing steadily, although it is difficult to know exactly what the facts are, since the whole matter is sometimes handled quietly.

As to the question of the efficacy of sterilization of the mentally defective, present day opinion inclines more and more to lack confidence in it as a measure for social control. It is unlikely to reduce the numbers of mentally deficient in succeeding generations, and it is no substitute for constructive training and community programs in the present.

RESEARCH

In recent years it has become sharply apparent that the classification of the mentally retarded is more of a hotchpotch than had heretofore been realized; that it includes many individuals who are mentally ill and not mentally defective, and who therefore ought to be receiving an entirely different type of treatment; and that some of the mentally retarded are defective in certain mental functions only — for instance, in the ability to understand spoken language — but not in all functions, and they are potentially educable when the right techniques can be found.

Just what the outlook is for significantly reducing the numbers of the mentally retarded is not clear as yet. Research has been proceeding on many fronts: into causes such as inherited metabolic and biochemical deficiencies; into the Rh factor and birth injury; into other adverse prenatal conditions such as German measles of the pregnant mother and factors causing congenital malformation and premature birth; and into surgical treatment of certain conditions such as hydrocephaly.

In general, it can be said that research into causes of mental deficiency is moderately encouraging, not to the extent of the extravagant hopes sometimes entertained for it by wishful parents but in a slow, steady increase of knowledge about the etiology of defect in a small percentage of cases.

NEEDS

Meanwhile, the care of the mentally retarded is certainly more dynamic than it used to be. Parent groups, another "citizens' movement," are becoming more articulate. Under the leadership of the National Association for Retarded Children, parents in many communities are bringing about improved facilities, especially for day care.

The most urgent needs of the mentally retarded are for adequate school classes in every community for children not requiring institutionalization; better training especially for those with only moderate degrees of retardation; differentiation of the mentally ill and the mentally retarded; and more research into causes.

VIII

At the Back of the Fronts

The Mentally Ill in Four Wars—
And After

ON JULY 18, 1918, when World War I was moving rapidly to its climax, the Chief of Staff of the United States Army in his office in Washington received a cablegram from the Commanding General of the American Expeditionary Force in France beginning:

> Prevalence of mental disorders in replacement troops recently received suggests urgent importance of intensive effort in eliminating unfit . . . prior to departure from U.S. . . .
>
> John J. Pershing

That cable has often since been credited as a turning point in acceptance by the military of the wisdom of heeding the recommendations of its neuropsychiatric advisers.

They replied immediately, pointing out that among the men recently sent overseas there were 3,035 whom they had recommended for discharge as totally unfit for military service for psychiatric reasons, and in a splendid military understatement, commented that this number, "thrust upon the service *en masse*," was enough to "tax the resources seriously."

WORLD WAR I

Actually, the climate for psychiatry was not bad during World War I. From the beginning, there was recognition of the necessity for providing facilities for the care of men who broke down while on duty overseas. Dr. Salmon, as Chief Psychiatrist of the American Expeditionary Force (AEF), had developed a plan which seemed to operate about as well as such a plan can operate in time of war. It came about this way.

Dr. Salmon had always been interested in military psychiatry, and as early as 1910, soon after he became a psychiatrist, he had written some articles on this subject. As 1917 approached and the entrance of the United States into the war seemed imminent, he saw what was coming and began putting the affairs of the National Committee for Mental Hygiene in shape so that he would be free to volunteer for active duty with the Public Health Service. In the process of informing himself about mental disorders in armies, he learned that in the U.S. Army on the Mexican border in 1916, 10 per cent of all discharges for disability had been for mental disorder and feeble-mindedness but that the Public Health Service had no plans for handling the problem in the approaching war.

In March 1917, a month before the United States declared war on Germany, Dr. Salmon and two associates went to see the Surgeon General (General William C.

Gorgas of Panama Canal Zone fame) to make some recommendations. General Gorgas was responsive. He sent them
on a tour of army camps and base hospitals on the Mexican
border, where they found that mental disorder was three
times as prevalent as in New York State. In April, they
submitted a comprehensive plan to General Gorgas, who
at once proceeded to establish a division of neuropsychiatry in the Public Health Service, and he put the National
Committee in charge of organizing psychiatric units. In
May, Dr. Salmon went to England to study how the British
were handling their "shell shock" cases, and in December
he sailed for France as Director of Psychiatry for the
American Expeditionary Force.

THE AEF

The system Dr. Salmon developed for the AEF is recognized today as a masterpiece of sound planning, comparable to the one which only after tragic confusion was
finally put into effect during the latter part of World War
II, and still more fully in the Korean War. Dr. Salmon's
plan included early recognition of mental and emotional
disturbances; prompt treatment as near the front as possible (this was one of the most important aspects); continued treatment by psychiatrists at a base hospital; a good
hospital at the ports of embarkation and debarkation; at
home, military hospitals in the nature of training schools;
psychiatrists attached to each Division to advise all medical
and line officers; and the elimination of the feeble-minded
from the service.

Under this admirable plan, soldiers who broke down on
active duty in France stood a good chance of getting better
psychiatric care there than they would have had at home,
and much better than they later received during the first
two years of World War II. (The names of the young psy-

chiatrists in France during World War I read like a roster of the elder statesmen of psychiatry today, and the same is true of World War II and of the Korean War. The men who made valuable contributions to the wars throughout the 1940's are the same men who are continuing to make valuable contributions to psychiatry today.)

Dr. Salmon himself, sensitive idealist that he was (though not a visionary), suffered in many ways during the war. "Thinking is about the most foolish thing a man can do when he is close up to a war," he wrote his superior officer — and this from a thinking man. Dr. Salmon also carried on several private wars of his own: against red tape; against the indifference of the people back home who could not grasp the urgency of the crisis; against the inaccurate and misleading term "shell shock," which he said conveyed a false impression of "mysteriously wounded heroes," and indeed against the whole concept of neurotic breakdown as a form of cowardice requiring punishment; against regulations requiring soldiers armed with rifles with fixed bayonets to stand guard in the observation ward of a mental hospital; and against a system (the Navy's) which permitted the gloriously simple classification of all mentally ill into two neat categories: "Insane, restraint; insane, other." (One shipload of 250 returning "shell shock" cases, most of whom were suffering from neuroses and required no supervision at all, were kept below decks on the whole trip across, without fresh air or exercise — shades of old Bedlam!)

History Repeats

All the great wealth of experience with psychiatry in World War I was summarized and published by the Medical Department of the U.S. Army in Volume X, entitled *Neuropsychiatry*, of the series of reports or "memoirs" on the medical services of the war. Dr. Salmon was one of the editors.

Then came World War II and all had been forgotten. Reportedly, the Surgeon General of the Army at that time did not know that Volume X was on his shelf. (According to reliable hearsay, the British military suffered a similar lapse of memory with respect to their own archives, but they discovered the American Volume X — which then became their bible — and it was they who called it to the attention of the U.S. Army Surgeon General.)

World War II

The early days of World War II make sad history from the point of view of what might have been expected in the way of enlightened management of mental breakdown in the second quarter of the twentieth century. A little handful of psychiatrists did some more pointing out. (Psychiatrists are often unable to do anything more than "point out" until people are ready to listen.) They pointed out the fact that every psychiatric casualty in World War I had cost American taxpayers $30,000 to date and the end was not yet in sight. They pointed out that three out of every five beds in the 79 veterans' hospitals were occupied by patients with nervous and mental diseases. They pointed to the compendium of experience in Volume X, and its companion Volume XV, which had all the data on mental tests. They begged to be permitted to put their knowledge to use in the selection of men, in the treatment of those who broke down, in the management of discharges, in programs for rehabilitation, and in problems of morale. But what few abortive efforts there were ended in chaos.

Soon, however, the realities of the situation began to force themselves on the attention both of the military and the civilian population. Even before anyone had an inkling of the magnitude of the problem of neuropsychiatric rejections and discharges, stories began to come through which showed what can happen when the rudiments of psychiatric screening are ignored. The following are examples:

A draftee who broke down five weeks after induction was found to have been schizophrenic for ten years — a patient in four different mental hospitals, having been discharged earlier from the Naval Academy at Annapolis because of a nervous breakdown.

In another case of a soldier who murdered three women in Australia, inquiry through the Social Service Exchange revealed voluminous records on the man and his family in a family agency, a state hospital, two reformatories, two parole agencies, and a number of relief agencies.

Clearly something was wrong at the induction centers.

SELECTION

Psychiatrists have never pretended to be crystal gazers. When at the induction centers they were required to interview two hundred, and at some centers as many as four hundred men a day, averaging one to five minutes per "interview," the so-called "psychiatric examination" became a farce, certainly due to no fault of the psychiatrists. Although Selective Service had agreed that a psychiatrist would be allotted fifteen minutes per interview, it was never possible to carry this out. Because the psychiatrists rarely had an opportunity to utilize the skills in which they were trained, much misunderstanding arose about what they could be expected to discover about a man (in two minutes!).

To the professional people who were accustomed to assessing personality disorder, it was apparent from the beginning that screening would be vastly more effective if social histories on registrants were available to the medical examiners at the induction centers, whether they were psychiatrists or general physicians. In the two cases cited above, the significant facts in the backgrounds of the men would have been unlikely to emerge in a two- or three-minute interview, but they would have shown up immediately in a social history prepared by a professional worker. Later in the war, a study of neuropsychiatric discharges was made, in which it was demonstrated that in 50 per cent of the cases the social history, if used, would have shown that the draftee was a bad risk and should have been rejected.

In the first days of the war, Selective Service had issued a directive to local draft boards urging them to seek further social data about registrants known to have a history of mental disease or poor social adjustment. Since no funds were provided, however, the directive was largely ignored except in a few cities and states which mobilized local resources to make a routine check of mental hospitals and a few other records. As the war progressed and the disastrous results of inadequate psychiatric screening became apparent, Selective Service was obliged to seek some remedies.

Once again the National Committee for Mental Hygiene stepped in. First it demonstrated that the use of case histories was feasible and then it sent a representative to Washington to work with Selective Service in developing procedures for obtaining them. Finally, in October 1943 (although by then seven or eight million men had gone through the draft process), Selective Service adopted the medical survey, which provided for the appointment of trained social workers and public health nurses as medical field agents attached to local boards and charged with the responsibility of compiling pertinent social and health information about registrants. Although the system never worked really well, it was better than no histories at all, and before the end of the war the services of several thousand social workers and public health nurses were utilized in obtaining histories on some million or so men.

CARE

As the pace of the fighting increased, so also, of course, did the number of breakdowns. At first there was no plan for the care of the men who broke down, either in this country or in the forward areas. Plans had to be developed while the fighting was going on. And once more it was necessary to learn what had already been learned in World War I: the importance of skilled treatment near the front as soon as possible after the breakdown, preferably within a few hours.

The problem of training enough physicians to provide psychiatric care was of course enormous. At the time of Pearl Harbor, in December 1941, there were thirty-five psychiatrists in the Regular Army Medical Corps. By 1945, there were 2,400 men practicing psychiatry, a growth which was made against great odds.

CONSULTATION

One of the most progressive steps was the development of a consultant system under which psychiatrists were assigned, along with surgeons, to each theatre of war and to each Service Command in the United States. In December 1943, Lieutenant Colonel (later Brigadier General) William C. Menninger became director of the Neuropsychiatric Consultants Division in the office of the Surgeon General of the Army. In the Navy, Commander Francis J. Braceland held a comparable position, and both men were responsible for creative and effective planning.

It is impossible here to do more than mention a few illustrative examples of the contributions of psychiatrists to the war effort. On the matter of discharges, for instance, it was discovered that so much stigma had become attached to an "n.p." (neuropsychiatric) discharge that it interfered with a man's finding employment. Upon the recommendation of psychiatrists, the "n.p." classification was therefore discontinued and it was required that the diagnosis be specified. With respect to morale, again it was necessary to relearn an old, old lesson: that morale is higher where leadership is strong, and that people who understand people make better leaders than people who do not. Accordingly, series of lectures were developed for line officers and enlisted men to try to give them some of the fundamentals of the psychiatric and psychological concepts behind human behavior and personality adjustment.

As to therapy, although no new types came out of the war experience, several were developed farther than they had been theretofore, and they later constituted an important contribution to therapy in civilian life. These were hypnosis; therapy under sedation such as pentothal (the so-called "truth serum," although it is not a serum, and may or may not induce the patient to tell the truth); group therapy; and treatment in convalescent hospitals.

WORDS

Once again one observes changes in vocabulary as denoting changes in attitude and understanding. During the Mexican border fighting, officials were concerned about "malingering." During World War I, this became "shell shock." In World War II, it was "combat fatigue" or "combat exhaustion" — terms which World War II psychiatrists selected, not because physical fatigue was a major factor, but in order to convey the idea of quick recovery, since fatigue and exhaustion are conditions a soldier gets over after a few days' rest. By the end of World War II and during the Korean War, "neuropsychiatric" and "psychoneurotic" were commonly used terms. (Neuropsychiatric refers to the entire gamut of personality disorders including psychosis, neurosis, behavior disorders, alcoholism, drug addiction, convulsive and other neurological disorders, and sometimes but not always it includes mental retardation; psychoneurotic or psychoneurosis is synonymous with neurotic or neurosis and is a specific diagnosis of certain types of mental disorder usually less severe than psychosis.)

REJECTIONS AND DISCHARGES

Figures about the numbers of neuropsychiatric rejections and discharges came as a stunning blow to the American people: one and three quarter million men rejected for military service because of mental and emotional disabilities and three quarters of a million more prematurely separated from the Service for the same reasons.

Perhaps it is worthy of comment that the rejection figures may be several times higher than they might have been under different circumstances, such as more thorough induction examinations and more effort at placing men with minor disabilities, as was done in countries where limited manpower was a greater problem than it was in the United States. Rejection figures, therefore, should not be taken at face value, but discharge figures can be. Even so, with or without the correct interpretation, these figures proved to have important educational value for the American people. Since World War II, there has been perceptibly more understanding of the nature and magnitude of mental illness, traceable at least in part to what was learned during the war.

POSTWAR

It is a well-known phenomenon of postwar periods that a grateful nation feels inspired to loosen its purse strings to provide generous benefits for its returning heroes — for a while. But it is hard to maintain gratitude at a high emotional pitch very long, and when it wanes the budget suffers.

In line with this national tendency, medical services for veterans, which had taken a spurt after World War I, deteriorated somewhat between the wars.

VETERANS' ADMINISTRATION

After World War II, thanks to strong and constructive leadership, excellent psychiatric services were established under the Veterans' Administration. Professional personnel — always a crying need — was trained in unprecedented numbers, and the high quality of the services set a new standard for the care of mental patients which was reflected in state hospitals throughout the country.

Partial safeguards against deterioration were built in through policies such as incorporating programs of research and training in every V.A. hospital, and locating the hospitals near important medical centers with which close working relations were maintained.

By the middle 1950's, V.A. hospitals were caring for almost 10 per cent of hospitalized psychiatric patients in the U.S. (about 54,000) with a waiting list (some 16,000 in 1955) growing longer each year. In addition V.A. outpatient services (mental hygiene clinics) were treating about 25,000 patients a year, and neuropsychiatric examining units were providing 125,000 examinations a year.

REHABILITATION

The period after World War II also saw an increase in organized efforts toward more effective rehabilitation of the mentally ill. Part of this was stimulated by experiences in the convalescent care of soldiers during the war, when it was realized as never before how important it is not to let convalescent mental patients sit around the wards in pajamas and robes with nothing to do. There were some striking demonstrations of the differences in speed of recovery of those for whom an active program was arranged and those who merely sat around.

Another stimulus toward rehabilitation came from a few small groups who were sensitive to the plight of the mental patient recently discharged from a hospital, not yet well enough adjusted to work, suffering from the stigma of having been in a mental hospital, often having no social life at all, sometimes without even a place to live. Many mental hospitals had no social service departments and many still have none. Those that had, never had enough staff to cope with this problem, and few other social agencies took an interest. One of the earliest groups was WANA ("We Are Not Alone") in New York City, which was later reorganized and became Fountain House, and is now carrying on a fine constructive program for former mental patients.

Rehabilitation was given still further impetus by certain federal action. The Barden-LaFollette Act, which for years had provided for the rehabilitation of the physically handicapped, was revised in 1943 with omission of the word "physical," thereby making federal funds available for the rehabilitation of the mentally handicapped. A Rehabilitation Office was set up in the Federal Security Administration to implement the Act. Just before the end of World

War II, the National Committee for Mental Hygiene established a Division of Rehabilitation which was at first concerned with returning veterans, but presently was broadened to include activities for the vocational rehabilitation of the mentally handicapped in the civilian population as well.

CONFERENCES

A phenomenon of the postwar period was the apparent urge professional people felt both to talk and to "do something." Many of them had had military experiences which moved them deeply. They had seen how great the potential contribution of psychiatry was, how great the need was, and how regrettable the deficiences were. The year 1946 saw a rash of important conferences, several of which grew into a continuing series. The Josiah Macy, Jr. Foundation, which had been experimenting with conferences for several years, stepped up its "conference program" to provide a forum for high-level scientific discussion among representatives of different disciplines. Most of the Macy conferences (some 150 up to 1960) were on medical subjects, but a number of them were on mental health or on medical subjects with mental health implications.

Beginning also in 1946, the Commonwealth Fund originated a series of teaching institutes for physicians, which had as their goal the integration of mental health concepts into pediatric practice, public health, and general medicine. Several important books emerged from this series, including the widely used *Public Health Is People* by Ethel L. Ginsburg.

A third series of discussions which was begun in 1946, under the leadership of William C. Menninger, M.D., became the Group for the Advancement of Psychiatry (GAP), an organization which has continued to influence American psychiatry up to the present. Originally regarded as the "Young Turks," this was a group of younger men in psychiatry, most of whom had seen active war duty and who were revolting against what they regarded as the ultra-conservatism of the American Psychiatric Association at that time, although since then their program has become integrated with that of the APA. The activities of this group have constituted one more step by which psychiatry has moved away from exclusive preoccupation with mental institutions and the mentally ill in the direction of concern for normal people and thus into social action. The "GAP Reports" cover a wide range of complex and often controversial problems, and some of them are making significant contributions to the social problems of our time. To mention one only, "GAP 37," entitled *Psychiatric Aspects of School Desegregation,* is a scholarly analysis remarkable for its depth and objectivity and now widely used by strategic professional and citizen groups throughout the country.

A fourth series of conferences, the Mental Hospital Institute, which started in 1949, demonstrates the full swing of a circle. As has already been pointed out, the American Psychiatric Association originated as an organization of mental hospital superintendents. (They now prefer to be called hospital directors.) Mental hospital matters continued to be a primary concern of the Association throughout its early years (as indicated, for instance, by the fact that when Dr. Salmon was elected president in 1923, he was the first president in the Association's 74 years who was not a superintendent of a mental hospital). Then with the "emergence of psychiatry" the programs at APA's annual meetings gradually became so broad that hospital psychiatrists began to feel their special interests were neglected. Furthermore, by the middle 1940's some of the more energetic and articulate of the war-experienced psychiatrists were realizing that hospital psychiatry was a national disgrace. Accordingly, the Mental Hospital Institute was created as part of the APA to provide a forum for the interchange of experience among hospitals. The Institute convenes for several days each Fall, and its several hundred participants include hospital personnel in all the professional categories and representatives of appropriate government departments.

IX

The One-World Theme

International Mental Health

"OFFICIAL consultative status with UN and its specialized agencies" might have sounded like gobbledygook to Clifford Beers because he could not possibly have known what the words meant, but the idea would have clicked with him as indeed it also would have delighted Dr. Salmon, Dr. Williams, Dr. Welch, Dr. Meyer, and all the early planners. They would have recognized in it the possibility of influencing opinion in high places to the benefit of the mentally ill, which is now one of the important functions of the present World Federation for Mental Health, direct descendant of Clifford Beers' original International Committee for Mental Hygiene.

FIRST CONGRESS

As early as 1919, Beers had begun to try to implement his dream of a world-wide mental hygiene movement.

That year he called together an organizing committee for an International Committee for Mental Hygiene, but it was not until eleven years later, in 1930, that the First International Congress on Mental Hygiene was held in Washington, D.C., with more than 3,000 participants representing some 50 countries.

The Congress was an impressive show. Nothing like that number of people had ever before assembled in the name of mental hygiene. Like other displays of public enthusiasm, the excitement generated had a value in focusing attention on the subject, although some of the leaders were frank in expressing their doubts as to whether the solid gains for the mentally ill were commensurate with the fanfare. Dr. Welch, who was usually enthusiastic about the mental hygiene movement, wrote in a letter to Dr. Simon Flexner immediately following the Congress in May 1930:

That big mental hygiene congress which I attended recently in Washington was rather terrible and an example of arousing the public before the foundation of sound knowledge and doctrine has been laid. With good psychiatric and neurological institutes something might be done in mental hygiene, but it would have to be at first so elementary as to lack altogether the spectacular appeal now made for the subject.

OTHER COUNTRIES

Throughout the 1920's and 1930's, Clifford Beers traveled extensively and carried on a voluminous correspondence encouraging people in other countries to organize national mental hygiene societies. Finland, in 1917, had been the second country after the United States to form a National Society, and Canada, in 1918, the third, thereby making the movement "officially international," as Beers later said. The third medical director of the National Committee for Mental Hygiene, Clarence M. Hincks, M.D. was also medical director of the Canadian Society at the same time. The next national society was the Union of South Africa, in 1919; after that, twenty-one more countries had formed societies by the time of the 1930 Congress.

In 1937, there was a second International Congress in Paris. From 1930 through World War II some of the national societies had ongoing programs but some existed principally on paper and there was little that could be called "international" in the sense of an exchange between nations.

WORLD FEDERATION FOR MENTAL HEALTH

Early in 1947, the International Committee for Mental Hygiene was reactivated, and elaborate plans were set in motion to hold a large Third International Congress on Mental Health in London in August 1948.

The United States played an active role in the preliminary work for the Congress. With Frank Fremont-Smith, M.D., as chairman of the interim governing board of the International Committee, and the present writer as the Committee's executive officer, a strong and active group of mental health leaders mobilized the participation of several thousand professional workers in "preparatory commissions" whose findings were later reported to the Congress in London.

Comparable preparatory commissions were at work in other countries throughout the year before the Congress. An important "International Preparatory Commission," with representatives from some dozen or so countries, met at Roffey Park in Sussex, England, for two weeks prior to the Congress to prepare what was modestly called a "Statement," a rather remarkable document which has been widely quoted and which still stands up today, with its solidly thought-through analysis of the status of world mental health and its lofty ideals, tempered by down-to-earth recommendations about what ought to be done.

At the Congress, according to the plan which had been worked out during the preceding year, the functions of the International Committee were taken over by the World Federation for Mental Health, which had been created upon the recommendation of United Nations' World Health Organization and UNESCO because they needed a nongovernmental mental health organization with which they could cooperate. (The old International Committee had been primarily psychiatric; the new Federation was set up as an interprofessional, multidiscipline organization from the beginning.)

John R. Rees, M.D., formerly Brigadier General and distinguished Senior Consultant in Psychiatry to the British Army during World War II, who was the prime mover behind both the Congress and the World Federation, was elected president of the Federation and has continued as its executive head up to the present. In 1960, the World Federation had member associations in 43 countries.

On World Health Day, in April 1959, the Federation proclaimed World Mental Health Year, which was to continue through 1960; its results are to be reported at an International Congress on Mental Health in Paris in the summer of 1961. For World Mental Health Year, six major areas, each headed by a co-ordinator of internationally recognized professional stature, were delineated as follows: World-wide Study of Childhood Mental Health, Cross-cultural Surveys of Attitudes Toward Mental Disorder, Mental Health Teaching in Professional Education, Mental Health and Developing Industrialization, Psychological Problems of Migration, and Psychological Problems of Aging.

Having official consultative status with the United Nations and several of its specialized agencies, the World Federation for Mental Health is in a position to influence some of UN's decisions and some aspects of its program. The two UN agencies with which the World Federation works most closely are the World Health Organization (WHO) and the United Nations Educational, Scientific and Cultural Organization (UNESCO).

The first director of WHO, and indeed quite literally its "creator," was a prominent Canadian psychiatrist, Brock Chisholm, M.D., formerly Director General of the Canadian Army Medical Services. Since its inception, WHO has made significant contributions to world mental health through the reports of its various Expert Committees; through some of its other special reports, such as the notable monograph *Mental Health and Maternal Care* by John Bowlby, M.D.; and through the widespread activities of its Mental Health Division, of which the British psychiatrist Ronald G. Hargreaves was the first director.

From the point of view of toilers in the mental health movement, both UNESCO and WHO got off to a brilliant start in the sentiments proclaimed by their founders. The UNESCO constitution contains that splendid sentence which, when it first appeared, seemed to strike some people with the force of conversion: "Since wars begin in the minds of men, it is in the minds of men that the defenses of peace must be constructed." And WHO, at its founding conference, adopted the lofty definition of health formulated by Dr. Chisholm as "a state of complete physical, mental and social well-being and not merely the absence of disease or infirmity," thereby placing mental and social health beside physical health as the objective for all health work.

X

The People: Of and By

*Legal Protection of the Mentally Ill
and Government's Expanding Role*

IF, IN extenuation of his behavior, a defendant pleads that he was temporarily the victim of an overwhelming urge to steal women's underwear or set fires or expose himself, was he suffering from an "irresistible impulse" or merely from an impulse that was not resisted? If a man suddenly goes berserk and kills a dozen people, did he "know right from wrong"? Was he aware of "the nature and consequences of his act"? At his trial who will be permitted to testify as a psychiatric expert? What are judge and jury to do if experts disagree?

These are just a few of the problems in determining the legal responsibility of the insane, which, incidentally, for the first thirty or forty years of American psychiatric literature called forth more words than any other single subject. Many well-intentioned legal decisions have raised more questions than they have solved. And many basic problems are still dangling.

"Irresistible Impulse"

The concept of the "irresistible impulse" has been accepted in some states since 1844, and it is now part of the law in 17 states. There is no question but that patients suffering from certain forms of neurosis may commit acts they struggle against, but these are usually noncriminal acts. The problem becomes especially important in homicide. Psychiatrists do not, however, consistently agree on the relation between irresistible impulse and homicide. Some of them point out the fact that the defendant was usually able to resist his impulses until such time as a policeman was not at his elbow. Most of them admit that medical testimony is on shaky ground if it tries to prove that impulses to steal or to harm others are irresistible. (But if psychiatrists admit puzzlement over some of these medical and ethical problems, the public does not, as indicated by the loud and emotional pronouncements on court cases "tried in the newspapers.")

"Right and Wrong"

The "right and wrong" test, which is even more complex than the "irresistible impulse," goes back to the seminal M'Naghten case in England in 1843, in which a paranoiac who had killed the secretary of Prime Minister Sir Robert Peel was acquitted on the ground of insanity. Because the verdict was unpopular, fifteen judges were summoned before the House of Lords to express their opinions. In their formal "Answers," they made the statement that "the party accused was laboring under such a defect of reason, from disease of the mind, as not to know the nature and quality of the act he was doing, or if he did know it that he did not know he was doing what was wrong." And that was the beginning of a hundred years of legal controversy on both sides of the Atlantic.

Although the M'Naghten rule has been subject to mounting criticism, it is still an important criterion of criminal responsibility in most states. It was not until 1954 that a new test, the Durham decision, was produced which is psychiatrically more defensible and which may eventually supersede the archaic M'Naghten rule. The Durham decision states that "an accused is not criminally responsible if his unlawful act was the product of mental disease or mental defect." Thus, under this test, culpability is determined, not on the basis of some hypothetical state of mind of the defendant, but by a judgment as to whether the offense emanated from the mental illness.

PSYCHIATRIC TESTIMONY

Many conscientious psychiatrists are reluctant to testify in court for a number of good reasons, chief of which perhaps is the danger of being drawn into a "battle of the experts," which makes them look foolish and brings discredit on their profession. The dilemma is by no means insoluble, however, when proper procedures are observed. The admirable pioneering Briggs Law in Massachusetts in 1921 cut through the problem by providing that for certain specified offenses the defendant shall be examined by two psychiatrists assigned by the State Department of Mental Diseases, and their report shall be made available to the defendant, the prosecution, and the court.

The state of New York, in 1930, further implemented this type of procedure by establishing "Qualified Examiners in Psychiatry," whose qualifications are determined by a state board. Few other states as yet have such safeguards for determining who is a psychiatric expert and how he shall be used. It is therefore up to the psychiatrists themselves to avoid the battle of the experts. No one will deny that the defendant must have the privilege of expert testimony, but psychiatrists can stay out of the trap and still fulfill their moral obligations if they are wise enough to follow the principles of the Briggs law and testify only on the request of the court and with the court bearing costs.

COMMITMENT

Commitment laws, which differ widely from state to state, present still another set of problems. Interestingly enough, "railroading" a sane person into a mental hospital, which is sometimes a fear of the uninformed public (exacerbated by occasional sensation-mongers) and which is theoretically possible, is not really a problem today. What is more of a problem is how to protect the patient, the public, and custodial officials, without harming the patient either by taking away his civil rights more than necessary or by causing him more than necessary suffering.

Traditionally, commitment procedures have resembled criminal procedures, as seen in the very terminology of commitment which has been widely prevalent until recently: a mentally ill patient was "arrested," "accused," put on trial on a "charge" of insanity, and if "guilty," he was "convicted" of insanity.

Since the beginning of the mental health movement, attorneys and other professional and citizen groups have been struggling to abolish archaic commitment procedures. But law reform moves slowly, and many states are still far behind the times in their practices. Some states, however (New York State is one), are encouraging the use

of voluntary commitment and admission by medical cer-
tificate, thereby eliminating the traumatizing experience of
court commitment for all cases except those where it is
clearly necessary.

In 1952, the National Institute of Mental Health, in an
effort to be helpful to state governments, formulated a
model Draft Act covering admission procedures, but for a
variety of reasons it has not been widely used and states
are now encouraged to work out their own acts.

DETENTION

Another aspect of the problem is the widespread practice
of detaining mental patients in jails pending admission to
a mental hospital, either by permission of the law or in
contravention of it. New York State, for instance, since
1827 has had a law prohibiting detention in jail, and yet
two studies, one in 1909 and one in 1925, showed that
nearly 20 per cent of patients admitted to state hospitals
had been detained in jails before commitment. Although
the situation is better than it used to be, some of the exposés in the 1940's indicated that the number of mentally
ill in jails would shock the public if all the facts were
known; and those whose duty it is to peer into our country's darker corners assure us that this situation still exists
in the 1960's. The problem will improve only as an enlightened public provides more adequate facilities for
proper detention before commitment, especially psychiatric beds in general hospitals.

RESTRAINT

The safeguarding of patients once they are in the hospital is less a matter for legislation than for regulation
through professional standards of care, although laws are

important, especially in preventing abuses in the use of mechanical restraints such as straitjackets.

The matter of mechanical restraint has been controversial for centuries. The main argument against it was succinctly summarized as early as the second century A.D. by a Greek physician who said, "Means of restraint imposed without management increases and even originates fury instead of calming it." But conscientious proponents of restraint have also expressed themselves. At the time of the founding meeting of the American Psychiatric Association in 1844, the topic was regarded as urgent enough to be chosen as the Association's first official proposition: "Resolved, that it is the unanimous sense of this convention that the attempt to abandon entirely the use of all means of personal restraint is not sanctioned by the true interests of the insane." And so for the next fifty years restraint became a subject of argument in almost every meeting of the APA.

Some of Clifford Beers' graphic descriptions of what he suffered from straitjackets point up the basic problem, which is less the use than the abuse of restraint. It was not until 1911 that the first law regulating restraint was passed (in Massachusetts). An example of a desirable type of regulation is to be found in the "general orders" governing protective restraint and seclusion in institutions as formulated by the New York State Department of Mental Hygiene, which specify that restraint or seclusion shall be used only by order of a physician, for medical reasons or to prevent a patient from injuring himself or others; and that a full record shall be kept which shall be subject to inspection by authorized persons.

In the last few years, the use of tranquilizers has changed the face of the problem substantially, but even so, vigilance will be required to the end of time to make certain that hospital patients are not harmed by the improper use of restraint.

STATE CARE

"State care," in the sense of mental patients as wards of the body politic, has been an accepted principle in the United States since the middle 1700's. In the late 1800's, considerable controversy raged over the relative merits of county care versus state care, "state" in the sense of state government. Beginning in its first year, the National Committee for Mental Hygiene pressed for the principle of complete state care, that is, mental institutions to be owned and operated by state governments.

Today a few states utilize county care in addition to state care. In most states, however, full responsibility is assumed by the state government, which builds and operates its own institutions. The magnitude of the task is apparent when one recalls that 50 per cent of all hospital beds are occupied by mentally ill patients — in round figures about 750,000.

State governments are showing more and more concern for the mentally ill. Examples of this are seen in the excellent report of the Council of State Governments in 1949 entitled *The Mental Health Programs of the Forty-eight States* and in the large amount of time the Council has been devoting to the subject of mental illness in the years since 1949. Another example is the number of state legislatures which have invited Dr. William C. Menninger to appear before them to interpret the needs of the field (seventeen such appearances to mid-1960). Still another is the fact of the very great increase in full-time mental health personnel employed by state governments in recent years.

FEDERAL RESPONSIBILITY

In the federal government, significant developments affecting the mentally ill have occurred in every decade since 1908. The following are illustrative only. During and after World War I, important new responsibilities were assumed for the first time by the Public Health Service. In the 1920's, the Bureau of the Census took over statistical reporting and accounting (now carried by the National Institute of Mental Health). In the 1930's, ten million dollars of Public Works Administration funds were spent on mental hospital construction. In the 1940's, after World War II, came the development of the excellent psychiatric hospitals of the Veterans' Administration.

Then, in 1946, occurred what was perhaps the most important event since the beginning of the mental health movement: the passage of the National Mental Health Act. This Act was sponsored by the National Committee for Mental Hygiene whose staff and other representatives had been working on the bill since 1940 — drafting and redrafting, appearing at congressional hearings, mobilizing support, and interpreting implications.

NATIONAL INSTITUTE OF MENTAL HEALTH

The act greatly expanded the functions of the Mental Hygiene Division of the Public Health Service, which in 1949 was reorganized and became the National Institute of Mental Health (NIMH), one of the National Institutes of Health of the Public Health Service which was then under the Federal Security Administration, now the Department of Health, Education, and Welfare.

Having started with relatively modest sums the first few years, in 1960 Congress voted $100,900,000 for the National Institute's 1961 budget, showing once again that government will loosen the purse strings when a project has the backing of the people. NIMH makes grants in three categories: for research; for professional training, especially of psychiatrists, clinical psychologists, psychiatric social workers, mental health nurses, and research personnel; and for the development of community mental health programs. Most of the research grants are awarded through institutions. Grants to states for community services are on a matching formula with the state required to match federal funds dollar for dollar.

In the few short years of its existence, the National Institute is able to point to a gratifying increase in the number of professional personnel available as a result of its training-grant program. Research has been stepped up and community services too are markedly increased, part of this directly due to NIMH although of course other forces have also entered in. Robert Felix, M.D., director of NIMH, is given much credit for the development of the impressive federal program. (Dr. Felix was installed as president of the American Psychiatric Association in the spring of 1960.)

COMMUNITY MENTAL HEALTH SERVICE ACTS

At the local level, a recent important development is the device for encouraging the expansion of community facilities by offering subsidies out of state funds through Community Mental Health Services Acts. New York State was the pioneer in 1954 with the first Community Mental Health Services Act, under which the state agreed to reimburse local communities for one-half of the amount they had spent (originally up to one dollar per capita; in 1960 increased to $1.20) for new mental health programs and improvement, and for the expansion of existing services, including psychiatric services in general hospitals, psychiatric clinics, psychiatric rehabilitation, and consultant and educational services to schools, courts, and health and welfare agencies. Since 1954, a number of other states have passed comparable acts, although provisions vary widely from one state to another.

Complications in administering state-wide community mental health service acts are very great indeed, with the danger of two closed systems (state and local community) competing with each other for funds and personnel, plus the almost insuperable difficulties attendant upon establishing laws and policies workable in both urban and rural communities.

CHANGING CONCEPTS

The past decade has seen dramatic increase in the use of public monies for such services as community clinics, rehabilitation, the training of professional personnel, research, and public education. In all these governmental activities, significant changes of concept are recognizable. One is recognition of the need for mental patients to be cared for early and near home rather than out-of-sight, out-of-mind in some vast isolated central facility. Another is the concept of government responsibility not only for the mentally ill in institutions, but for all the mentally ill wherever they are. Still another, growing out of the idea of prevention, is the concept of government responsibility not only for those who are already mentally ill but for the mental health of all the people.

XI

Outreach

Psychiatric Concepts Pervade
the Helping Professions

IT IS of course impossible to assign a date to any specific period when mental health ideas began to take hold in the professions. The process was gradual but by no means slow. As psychiatrically oriented workers began to realize how many human problems might be prevented if more people had more understanding of what the workers regarded as "mental health principles," they became eager to spread their knowledge. Concomitantly, as people without psychiatric orientation observed how many of the problems they met in their work could be helped by the application of the same "principles," they began to reach out for more understanding. Thus it came about that one after another the professions concerned with people began to dip into the richness of the newly developing psychiatric concepts and to apply what they could to their own work. At the same time, each profession brought insights of its own to enrich the growing field of mental health.

THE HELPING PROFESSIONS

In mental health, it has long been customary as a matter of convenience to divide the helping professions into two groups: the core professions in mental health and the related professions.

The core professions include those in which training has equipped the members to work directly with emotionally disturbed people. Originally (beginning around 1920 or a little later), core professions meant psychiatrists, clinical psychologists, and psychiatric social workers — the psychiatric team. More recently, psychiatric nurses and psychiatric aides are also being given the recognition they deserve as members of the team.

The related professions include doctors, nurses, teachers, ministers of religion, and law enforcement officials — professional workers whose primary responsibility is for healing, teaching or some other form of service to society. Although their training is not intended to equip them for dealing specifically with emotional disturbance, in the course of their work they inevitably find themselves obliged to cope with it. Furthermore, they are in a strategic position to play a constructive role in prevention and in "positive mental health."

Clearly, it would be possible to write a thick book on the role in the mental health movement of each of the helping professions. Psychiatry's role has been indicated throughout this account. The following are thumbnail sketches of a few developments selected quite arbitrarily to illustrate the interrelation of mental health and the professions.

PSYCHIATRIC SOCIAL WORK

Psychiatric social work as a profession took its rise during World War I. Beginning in 1914, E. E. Southard, M.D., director of the Boston Psychopathic Hospital (whose name is perpetuated today in the Southard School of the Menninger Foundation in Topeka, Kansas), and his chief psychiatric social worker, Mary C. Jarrett, had been conducting classes for half a dozen social workers to give them some psychiatric orientation. The National Committee for Mental Hygiene proposed that this type of training be extended further and formed a committee which included among others some of the same familiar names of the early leaders who have already appeared in this account — Dr. Russell, Dr. Fernald, Dr. Salmon, plus another distinguished name not usually associated with the early mental hygiene movement, President W. A. Neilson of Smith College. As a result, in the summer of 1918 a "training school for psychiatric social work" was opened at Smith College, the first of its kind, operated jointly by Smith College and the Boston Psychopathic Hospital under the auspices of the National Committee for Mental Hygiene, with Mary Jarrett as the director. (There are any number of "fathers" in the mental health movement, but Miss Jarrett is one of the few "mothers" — "mother of psychiatric social work.")

About the same period, the New York School of Social Work began including courses in psychiatric social work, and very shortly psychiatric social work was a full-fledged profession. So great has been its contribution to the mental health movement that it is impossible to conceive what the movement would have been like without it.

And indeed the same thing can be said for other branches of social work: medical social work, group work, child welfare, family welfare, and the rapidly growing field of public assistance administration. All of these have played a vital role in coping with the endless ramifications of mental illness, in efforts at prevention, and in furthering the mental health ideal.

Clinical Psychology

Although psychology was already recognized as a field of study well before the beginning of the century, it was almost entirely nonclinical and confined exclusively to the universities. In America, psychology as a profession experienced its first big spurt of growth following the introduction of intelligence tests, which, as has been mentioned, were brought to this country during the first decade of the century. The next big push came during World War I, when the Army Alpha was administered to one and three-quarter million men and people began to recognize the potentialities of mental tests. When child guidance clinics came along in the early 1920's, clinical psychology as a subdivision of psychology as a whole and clinical psychologists as members of the psychiatric team found their own special niche.

Professional psychology has contributed to many aspects of the mental health movement, but without question its greatest contribution has been in the development of mental tests, which are now so taken for granted that one forgets how many concepts had to be clarified before they could become the useful instruments they are today.

In the early days of testing, the idea of age-norms was still new; the differences between general intelligence of the kind the Stanford-Binet test was trying to measure and educational experience as indicated by achievement tests were not yet clear; tests of special ability had not yet been developed, nor had personality tests. Test results were alternately accepted with uncritical enthusiasm or rejected with undeserved scepticism. It took a good many years before they finally shook down into their proper place as valuable but by no means infallible diagnostic instruments.

Perhaps the most creative development of the last two decades has been the gradual refinement of "projective methods" (a term originated by Lawrence K. Frank in 1938). These are techniques for observing personality in which there are no right and wrong answers or measures of ability, but the subject "projects" his own interpretation on unstructured material. The Rorschach ink-blot test is the best known example. It is the projective techniques which have become the chief stock-in-trade of the now-mushrooming profession of clinical psychology, and which, especially since World War II, have been largely responsible for opening up to clinical psychologists the wide variety of different situations outside the traditional clinic and hospital where their new skills are being used to advantage.

Nurses and Attendants

Within the nursing profession, there has long been some provision for training in the specialty of psychiatric nursing, either offered as part of the training of a student nurse through affiliation with a mental hospital or else offered to registered nurses through graduate courses and in-service training. Here again, as with some of the other professions, although the number of trained psychiatric nurses is small, their influence on the field of nursing as a whole has been significant.

In a mental hospital, the person closest to the patient

is the attendant — not so many years ago still called guard or keeper. It requires little imagination to realize that this person — through his kindness or cruelty, along with his skill or lack of it — can either help the patient get well or create a hospital hell for him.

A perennial problem of all mental hospitals throughout the years has been the low pay of personnel, particularly attendants, and the consequent low caliber of employees willing to serve as attendants — many of them itinerants, ignorant, cruel, hating their work. This situation has changed considerably since World War II, with credit for some of the improvements going to the energetic efforts of the conscientious objectors who worked in mental hospitals under Selective Service during the war. (That story and the story of the National Mental Health Foundation which they later founded will be told in a subsequent chapter.)

MEDICINE

Among medical specialties, pediatrics has played a key role in mental health. Despite the fact that only 15 per cent of children in the United States are cared for by pediatricians, pediatric concepts have permeated general medicine, nursing, public health, and also non-medical fields such as teaching and institutional care.

It was in the early 1940's that a handful of pediatricians with psychiatric training began changing the conception of what constitutes good health care for children. Two of the best known among them were Benjamin Spock, M.D., later famous for his *Pocket Book of Baby and Child Care,* and Milton J. E. Senn, M.D., then at Cornell University Medical College and later at Yale. Dr. Spock's book, when it first appeared in 1946, was the most comprehensive integration of the psychological and the physical aspects of child care available to parents and professional workers up to that date, and it remains so up to this date. Dr. Senn influenced pediatric teaching through his convictions about the necessity of sensitizing medical students to the fact that early mother-child relationships are the foundation on which the child's later adjustment is built, and that helping mothers with the emotional and behavior problems of their children is part of the physician's responsibility for health care. In addition to formal teaching, some of his devices for incorporating a psychiatric orientation into the medical curriculum have included using a nursery school to teach medical students about the everyday problems of normal children, having students observe child guidance clinic procedures in a pediatric setting, and having them assume responsibility (supervised) for an entire family, including home visiting.

During this same period (the early 1940's), doctors and nurses in public health settings were becoming more sensitive to the fact that mothers of young children, once immunization is over and a diet of solid foods has been established, are more concerned about the psychological problems of their children than about physical care. Also, at about this same period, antibiotics began to reduce the acute illnesses of young children, thereby releasing both the time and the energy of pediatricians so that they were able to concern themselves more with children's behavior. By then, too, parents were beginning to demand more from their doctors in the way of psychological guidance. All these forces and still others, such as the rapidly growing body of literature in the field, have combined to broaden the concept of good health care of children to include psychological care.

If space permitted, similar changes could be traced in other medical fields, such as public health nursing, and general medicine itself, with the rapid acceptance of "psychosomatic" concepts. In the early 1940's, many physicians who were still resistant to what they would call "psychiatric" ideas, jumped at the less objectionable term "psychosomatic," although in their application the two words meant practically the same thing.

Of all the changes that might be mentioned, perhaps none is more important than those which have resulted in incorporating psychiatric content into all medical education, with medical students now introduced to psychiatric ideas in the first years of their training and with courses in psychiatry today an integral part of the curriculum in most medical schools.

The one medical field probably the farthest behind when it comes to incorporating mental health principles into practice is hospital administration, especially as it affects children. Here and there will be found enlightened efforts toward reducing the traumatic effects of hospitalization on young children, such as by preparing the children for what to expect, flexible visiting hours, and allowing the mothers to help care for them. In many places, however, hospital policies still fail to reflect the a-b-c's of modern mental health teaching.

TEACHER TRAINING

When E. K. Wickman's book *Children's Behavior and Teachers' Attitudes* appeared in 1928, his charts were a revelation. Table after table showed that what teachers regarded as signs of maladjustment in children, psychiatrists passed off as normal behavior, and vice versa. At the extremes ("most serious" and "least serious"), there was almost no overlap. Teachers were troubled by aggressiveness in all its forms and by any behavior which contravened the discipline of the classroom, now often referred

to as "acting-out behavior." Psychiatrists were more concerned about signs of withdrawing and evidence of a
child's inability to get along with his peers. All this was
"news," both to the teaching profession and to the recently
created clinic teams (Mr. Wickman himself was at that
time a psychologist with the Commonwealth Fund demonstration clinics) who were just then beginning to concern
themselves about the adjustment of children in school.
Wickman's book was one of the milestones in the long
educational process of teaching teachers about mental
health in the classroom.

By the middle 1930's, nursery education, which had
scarcely been heard of a decade earlier, was beginning to
make itself felt. From the point of view of mental health,
nursery school teachers have been one of the most receptive of the professional groups. Not only have they utilized
mental health principles with remarkable freshness and
consistency in their own work, but they have contributed
enormously to mental health with their sensitive percep-
tion of children's "needs," of what constitutes "good experiences," and of the dynamic quality of "development"
— all of these being terms they have endowed with rich
meaning.

The mental health field stands debtor to some of the
pioneering work in nursery and elementary education going on for the last twenty years in such places as the Department of Child Study at Vassar, and the Mills College
of Education and Bank Street College of Education in
New York. That mental health recognizes its debt is
suggested by at least one recent incident — the grant of a
million dollars in 1958 from the National Institute of
Mental Health to the Bank Street College of Education
for studies of mental health in the schools.

As to the subject of children's needs and the sequence of

their psychological development, one of the highly influential publications formulating these concepts definitively for the first time was the little pamphlet *Fundamental Needs of the Child* by Lawrence K. Frank, originally published in *Mental Hygiene* in 1938, later reprinted innumerable times and used in an incredibly wide variety of situations. An important book of the same period was *Emotion and the Educative Process* by Daniel A. Prescott, published by the American Council on Education in 1938, which for many educators was their first introduction to the subject. More recently Erik H. Erikson has reformulated the concepts and introduced them to a new generation of students, first as part of the working papers prior to the Mid-century White House Conference on Children and Youth in 1950, and then published as a book the same year under the title *Childhood and Society.*

For many years, the National Committee for Mental Hygiene carried on the teacher-training mission conscientiously through studies (a major one was initiated in 1935 under a grant from the Carnegie Corporation), through field service, and through its pamphlet and periodical literature, both *Mental Hygiene,* and its quarterly journal for teachers, *Understanding the Child,* edited by Carson Ryan (now discontinued).

RELIGION

For the last twenty-five years, articles, conferences, symposia, and committees on "Religion and Psychiatry" have been commonplace. The assumption usually seems to be that the writers or the participants will explore their common ground, yet curiously enough they rarely get around to discussing what religion has to offer psychiatry — surely a strange omission. What they do discuss invariably turns out to be what clergymen can learn from psychiatry that will help them in their daily contacts with

troubled people, a vital enough subject to be sure, and a
vast one, but not "religion."

Because clergymen traditionally counsel troubled people, many of them have actively sought to learn more
about psychiatry, and psychiatrists have been only too glad
to co-operate. The pioneering Council for Clinical Training, established in 1930, was the first center for clinical
pastoral training. Today, there are many places where
clergymen may receive training, usually in a hospital or
other institutional setting. Supervised work with individual cases and sometimes with groups is offered, the
supervisor usually being a clinically trained clergyman, not
a psychiatrist. Without trying to make clergymen into
amateur psychiatrists, these centers provide orientation in
the fundamentals of personality structure and emotional
disturbance, and they teach the clergyman how, through
better understanding of the troubled person and his family, he can become more helpful as a counsellor.

There are many other noteworthy developments in the
partnership of religion and psychiatry. To cite a few: both
the American Psychiatric Association and the Group for
the Advancement of Psychiatry have committees on psychiatry and religion. Some denominations require that candidates for the ministry be given a battery of psychological
tests both to rule out serious mental disturbance and as an
aid to self-knowledge. Psychiatrists on the faculties of theological seminaries are no longer a rarity. Some churches
and synagogues now operate psychiatric clinics and many
others will arrange psychiatric consultation for their con-
gregants. Many offer courses in family life education and
related subjects. The literature of psychiatry and religion
has grown to considerable proportions; two helpful peri-
odicals for interested clergymen are the *Journal of Pastoral
Care* and *Pastoral Psychology.* In 1954, the Academy of

Religion and Mental Health was established in an effort to promote some co-ordination of the joint concerns of the two fields.

LAW ENFORCEMENT

Police are sometimes called our "first line psychiatrists" because they are the ones who often must cope with a mentally ill person at a moment of acute crisis in his life — a threatened suicide, an alcoholic, a patient gone berserk. It was about 1919 that Dr. Salmon gave the first mental hygiene course for policemen, and in the years since then, many state and local mental health associations have experimented with courses for policemen as part of their programs.

It may seem something of an anomaly that despite the fact that child guidance clinics grew directly out of concern about juvenile delinquency, today juvenile delinquency is frequently regarded as falling outside the field of mental health, presumably because social factors outweigh psychological factors in the problem as a whole. True, in any individual case, psychological factors may be paramout. But in a large proportion of cases, all the psychiatric techniques in the book are futile until the underlying social deficiencies are remedied. Unlike psychosis, for which we do not know the causes, in delinquency we do know but we do not practice what we know.

In the 1920's, hopes were high that innovations such as children's and family courts, psychiatric clinics in prisons, and social work training for probation officers would mitigate some of society's failures in the management of its criminals. Today, despite constructive pieces of work being done here and there, the picture is dismal. Psychiatry has again done a lot of "pointing out" but has never been given (and has never seized) the opportunity to contribute more than a fraction of what it is capable of contributing.

XII

That He Who Runs May Read

Public Education,

Public Relations, and Fund-Raising

THE HISTORY of public education in mental health divides itself neatly down the middle of the fifty years of the movement, each quarter century having its own characteristics, and each having its own vocabulary. Indeed, the history of the entire movement might be written around vocabulary changes, indicating as they do changes in attitudes and ways of doing things (changes often for the better but not necessarily so).

Some of the words, and the ideas behind them, which are commonplace today would have sounded like another language to mental hygiene groups only a few decades ago:

"mass media of communication" and "audio-visual aids";
"public relations" and "press conferences"; "video," "kine-
scope," "tapes," "telethons" (all aimed at "the man in the
street" and his humble abode in "the grass roots"). Then
there are the catch terms of profound and disturbing significance for our times: "ghost writers," "hidden per-
suaders," "Madison Avenue techniques" (to say nothing
of "Madison Avenue bafflegab"). But perhaps most important of all for the field under discussion was the change
from "mental hygiene" to "mental health," which will be
discussed in the next chapter.

FIRST QUARTER CENTURY

With respect to mental health education, the most significant characteristic of the early period was the lack of
public interest. Mental hygiene societies were well satisfied
if more than a handful of people showed up at one of their
meetings — and if it rained they could scarcely count on
filling the two front rows. Finding a ballroom big enough
to accommodate the crowd was never a problem! Writers,
reporters, government officials, civic leaders — even educators — were conspicuous by their absence. When mental
hygiene enthusiasts tried to create interest in their subject,
the response they got used to hearing was "Mental Hygiene? What's that?"

Many of the professionals were messianic about their
work. They felt a strong urge to spread their knowledge
but they did not know the techniques of arousing public
interest. It did not occur to them to try to dramatize their
message, and they were more than a little afraid of too
much public interest anyway. Publicity was something that
happened — it was not planned — and though sometimes good, it was usually bad (or so they felt).

Clifford Beers liked to tell about a speech he gave in

1922, in which he made the statement that a student at Harvard or Yale who broke down then, in 1922, had a better chance of getting good psychiatric care than he, Beers, had had in 1900. According to Mr. Beers, the newspaper account reported him as having said that if he had gone to Harvard instead of Yale he would not have had a breakdown! Of course the remarkable thing is that there was a newspaper reporter present at all, for mental hygiene was rarely regarded as "news" in those days unless it was some sordid exposé. The twist given his words was only too typical of the attitude of the press and was one of the factors in the cold war between press and psychiatry which gradually built up within the next two to three decades — a war which is not yet over by any means, although tension decreases year by year as each group sees the desirability of co-operating with the other.

EARLY PUBLICATIONS

In the early years of the movement, there was a rapidly growing body of psychiatric literature but no mental hygiene or mental health literature, either periodical or pamphlet, of the type we take for granted today. Beginning in 1917, the pioneering quarterly *Mental Hygiene,* official publication of the National Committee for Mental Hygiene, was the first periodical which attempted to convey the new knowledge outside the core professions to the related professions and the general public. Except for occasional space devoted to child care, other professional journals and the popular press rarely carried an article that could be labeled "mental hygiene." Therefore many people received their first introduction to the subject through the pages of this modest journal, of which Frankwood E. Williams, M.D., was the first editor. Although its circulation was never large and it spoke chiefly to the "already convinced," as the official voice of the new field, it helped give shape to the entire movement. If it were possible to trace back, it would almost surely be found that ideas first appearing in *Mental Hygiene* provided the motivation behind many professional careers and many citizens' groups.

There was a long period from 1908 well into the 1930's when the pamphlet list of the National Committee for Mental Hygiene was the chief source of literature about mental hygiene. The first National Committee pamphlets appeared in 1912. After *Mental Hygiene* started, the sequence for many pamphlets was: a paper read at an annual meeting of the National Committee, then published in *Mental Hygiene,* and then reprinted as a pamphlet. Others were written specifically as pamphlets to fill needs recognized by the staff of the National Committee. Some of these were reprinted again and again, continuing in circulation up to twenty years or longer. (The more popular of the early pamphlets, *Your Mind and You* by George Pratt, M.D., for example, reached a large and important audience.)

Those early pamphlets look drab to us now. The type was small, the margins narrow, the paper inferior, and only a few were dressed up to the extent of having a self cover. No one thought about white space, coated paper, headings, color, or layout. The "slick jobs" which are admired today were unheard of then. But part of the reason was that the people responsible for them were preoccupied with the substance and not the appearance. Moreover, since the object was to have them used, they were made available at prices of 5, 10, or 15 cents, only occasionally soaring to 25 cents, to fit the slender purses of the impoverished professional workers for whom they were intended. There was a message to be put across — and those forthright little pamphlets played their part.

PARENT EDUCATION

Another significant body of mental hygiene literature — not usually called mental hygiene then, but appropriately subsumed under that heading as we look back at it now — was the material being published about the psychological aspects of child care. Two leading organizations were the Child Study Association of America, established in 1888 (then called the Society for the Study of Child Nature) and the United States Children's Bureau, established in 1912. There have been times in the last forty years when parent education went off into unfortunate bypaths, such as the regrettable excursion into "Behaviorism" in the 1920s (the idea that the child is a small machine and should be treated accordingly) and some of the excesses later committed in the name of permissiveness (in reaction against the proponents of the hairbrush-in-the-back-woodshed school of thought). But it is a matter of pride with these two organizations that they can look back on the ideas they have been promulgating and feel gratified by the consistency of their soundness, at least insofar as we are able to judge soundness today. Some of those early publications have had a remarkable history, such as the Children's Bureau pamphlet *Infant Care,* first published in 1914, now in its tenth edition, of which forty-two million copies have been distributed.

Pamphlet literature has played an important part in parent education, and some of the pamphlets distributed by the mental health associations in the 1930's and 1940's were sold in astonishing numbers, such as *Special Problems of Children: Aged 2 to 5 Years* by Nina Ridenour and Isabel Johnson (first published by the New York State Committee for Mental Hygiene) which topped the million mark, and was translated into a number of languages including Japanese.

A unique series was *Pierre the Pelican* by Loyd W. Rowland, Ph.D., published under the aegis of the Louisiana Society for Mental Hygiene. (In Louisiana it is not the stork, but the pelican who brings babies, and Pierre is a wise bird who gives excellent advice to parents, interspersed with helpful hints from his equally sagacious wife Pierette.) The series was in the form of monthly letters distributed by state health departments and mailed on the child's "month-day" to every parent of a first-born child in the state. Some dozen or more states have utilized the series, some of them continuing for more than ten years. In the thin years before the present avalanche of parent education material had accumulated, this series was probably among the most widely read mental health literature in the country. It is a prime example of mental health education through "homogeneous, highly motivated groups": that is, the method of singling out a total group and directing educational material to every member of the group (in this instance, all parents of first-born children) at a period in their lives when they are likely to be receptive to new ideas.

There was a long period when it did not occur to parent educators to question the validity of the ideas they were urging on parents. The last few years have brought a rash of self-examination by educators, to the point where efforts at evaluation can be mentioned as a significant trend of the present period. Although unquestionably a healthy trend, it cannot honestly be said that these appraisals have as yet produced any significant new ideas, and at least some of the "new" skepticism is distinctly unhealthy. Inability to prove that something *is* effective is not the same as proving that it is *not* effective, as is often naively assumed. Also, it is unfortunate when doubts and disagreements among authorities are played up and presented to the public as if there were no agreement at all, while the substantial body of knowledge on which authorities do agree is disregarded. True evaluation in parent education and in fact across the board in all mental health education, desperately as it is needed, is extraordinarily difficult to arrive at, and it is to be hoped that the future will produce appraisal techniques more effective than any that have been devised up to now.

Today the spontaneous reaching-out of parents (and of teachers) and their eagerness to learn and to share are apparent along many lines: in the almost overwhelming flood of parent-education literature; in the multiplicity of self-organizing parent groups; and in the widespread participation in more formal organizations, such as the National Congress of Parents and Teachers with its eleven and one half million members.

BOOKS

Some of the early first-of-their-kind books carried a tremendous impact. William A. White's *Outlines of Psychiatry,* for instance, published in 1907, introduced to American students the whole sweep of dynamic psychiatry — Freud's psychoanalytic concepts integrated with White's own profound insights, all in an intelligible, readable presentation. In his monumental study *One Hundred Years of American Psychiatric Literature,* in the American Psychiatric Association's centennial volume in 1944, Henry Alden Bunker said of that book, "In its first as in its fourteenth edition, White's book is the best 'Outline' of psychiatry without question in English." (Dr. White's name is commemorated for us today in the name of the William Alanson White Institute of Psychiatry, Psychoanalysis and Psychology in New York.)

Freud's own early works were also just coming out during this same period. His *Interpretation of Dreams,* which his official biographer, Ernest Jones, says was the best of all Freud's books, was published in German in 1900 and translated into English in 1913 by A. A. Brill, who did more than any other one person to introduce Freud to English readers. Freud's dramatic *Psychopathology of Everyday Life* in 1914 quickly made him known to a still wider audience.

In 1915 William Healy's epochal book, *The Individual Delinquent,* was the first to strike a telling blow against the then prevalent concept of the "born criminal" and to illustrate through several hundred colorful case histories the idea of the multiple causation of behavior. Southard and Jarrett's *Kingdom of Evils* in 1922 was another which look at delinquents — not from the point of view of their transgressions — but as human beings most of whom came from deplorable backgrounds.

One of the early "popular" books was the remarkable little pocket-size primer, *The Psychology of Insanity,* by Bernard Hart, in 1916, which for many years was to be found on every shelf. Another published the same year was William A. White's *Mechanisms of Character Formation,* which shaped the thinking of a full generation of students in psychology and social work, as well as psychiatry. Somewhat later (1930) came Karl Menninger's excellent book, *The Human Mind,* intended for the unoriented but serious reader, and never surpassed of its kind.

In 1930 Stanley Powell Davies' *Social Control of the Mentally Deficient* broke precedents by presenting the mentally retarded not as laboratory specimens but as people with problems which society could ameliorate through proper management. A definitive handling of the subject, and widely used as a text-book for many years, this book proved to be a practicum for social action. (In 1959 it was re-written and published under the title *The Mentally Retarded in Society*.)

Another book introducing new ideas to a new audience was *Emotions and Bodily Changes*, by H. Flanders Dunbar, in 1935, which, without raising the hackles of those still resistant to anything labelled psychiatric, managed to demonstrate the relevance of psychiatric concepts to medical practice.

Clearly, such listing could go on indefinitely if space permitted. The reader is invited to try his hand at his own list in this absorbing parlor game.

THE 1930's

In 1934, the National Committee for Mental Hygiene celebrated its twenty-fifth anniversary. There were meetings and speeches and more than a spate of publications. The book, *Twenty-five Years After: Sidelights on the Mental Hygiene Movement and Its Founder,* consisting of letters honoring Clifford Beers, was impressive in showing the esteem in which he was held and the large number of prominent people all over the world who were cognizant of the significance of the mental hygiene movement. A new edition of Beers' *Mind That Found Itself* was brought out with an historical summary by C.-E. A. Winslow, Dr.P.H. (In accordance with the stipulation in Mr. Beers' will, each new printing of *A Mind That Found Itself* is supposed to contain an appendix describing the developments of the mental health movement up to the date of publication. The last such historical summary was written by the present author for the book as "reprinted with additions" in 1953.)

By the 1930's, interest in mental hygiene was swelling rapidly among professional groups, if not yet among the lay public. Professional organizations in all the helping professions began to introduce mental hygiene topics at their meetings, and these invariably turned out to be the most crowded sessions, often to the annoyance of the program committee. No meeting room was large enough. The back rows of ballrooms were finally filled, as overflow audiences spilled out into the corridors.

Demands for professional service were in keeping. Throughout the depression years when unemployment was rife in many professions, trained workers in the several mental hygiene fields had their choice of good jobs. For instance, in February 1933, when the "bank holiday" in Detroit precipitated a financial crisis even more acute there than elsewhere, and the Detroit Children's Center, which was then the largest child guidance clinic in the country, found it necessary to discharge one-half of the staff with no notice at all, every member was placed in another position within two weeks.

The same forces which have been noted as accounting for the "outreach" described in the chapter on related professions were in the 1930's also becoming apparent in public education. People were reaching out, and professional workers were trying to communicate. But most mental hygiene education was still directed to the already oriented. It was not yet systematically aimed at the general public, who had never heard of the new ideas.

The 1940's

It was not until the 1940's that the term "mass media of communication" with all its implications began to be freely bandied about. The war years taught new skills in the techniques of mass communication and new convictions about the importance of "reaching people," and the end of the war released new energies for putting them into effect. Professional workers began to see the necessity of utilizing the skills of the people experienced in communication, and the communications people began to see that there was "news" in mental health after all. Whereas in the 1930's if a mental hygiene society happened to be sophisticated enough to hold a press conference, the staff waited in trepidation to see whether any reporters would show up — and many a time none did. And if a magazine writer stuck his head inside the office of a mental hygiene society with the thought of possibly "doing a story," the staff would fall all over themselves to be cooperative. By the 1940's, finding time to cope with writers, reporters, and producers had become a problem for professional staffs. As they became more communication-conscious, they saw the desirability of utilizing communications "expertise." Mental hygiene societies, heretofore satisfied with one underpaid jack-of-all-trades executive secretary, were now seeking public relations and fund-raising consultation, and trying to find the money to pay for it. They began to use publicity, not just occasionally or by chance, but consistently and planfully, as a device for interpreting their work to the public. At the same time, they began to recast their material for presentation through new and wider channels: press, radio, television, films, and drama.

In order to tell the story of the irruption of mental health into the mass media, it is necessary first to tell the story of the origins of the National Mental Health Foundation and the early efforts of its founders.

NATIONAL MENTAL HEALTH FOUNDATION

During World War II, the conscientious objectors in Civilian Public Service who, as a measure for relieving the acute personnel shortages, had been assigned by the Selective Service System to work in mental hospitals, were shocked by the appalling conditions they found there. Because many of them served as attendants, they quickly saw both the difficulties and the importance of the attendant's job, and they recognized the necessity of endowing his role with dignity if mental patients were to receive decent care. In the spring of 1944, a handful of them initiated an "exchange service," a little mimeographed bulletin called *The Attendant,* which they circulated among the three thousand conscientious objectors in some sixty mental hospitals. The bulletin not only met with immediate response and co-operation, but as reports began to pour in from conscientious objectors in other hospitals, the original group began to shape up some systematic plans for reform.

Largely because of the success of *The Attendant,* the American Friends Service Committee, in its liaison capacity between Selective Service and the churches which had initiated Civilian Public Service, persuaded Selective Service to give official approval to a mental hygiene program proposed by the conscientious objectors. Thus, from "a mental hygiene program" (with small letters), their plan soon became "the Mental Hygiene Program of Civilian Public Service," and, by authorization of Selective Service, was placed under the supervision of the National Committee for Mental Hygiene. During the war years, the core of their program was improving the caliber of attendants — or "psychiatric aides," a term they preferred to "attendants."

After the war, when the same group organized the National Mental Health Foundation (that part of their story will be continued in the next chapter), they expanded their efforts on behalf of attendants. As a successor to *The Attendant,* they published a regular journal, *The Psychiatric Aide,* and a handbook for aides. They established "Psychiatric Aide of the Year" awards and, in co-operation with others, developed the first training courses for aides.

From the beginning, the conscientious objectors shared the conviction that the deplorable conditions they witnessed were not, as was so often assumed, due to the negligence and indifference of incompetent superintendents, but rather to lack of funds which in turn was traceable to public apathy. Convinced that the public could be roused from its torpor if confronted by the full facts in all their sordid detail, the conscientious objectors conceived their role as one of awakening public conscience (memories of Clifford Beers!) They believed, moreover, that although all inadequacies should be fully exposed, this should be done only in a context of interpreting the reasons for bad conditions and collaborating with public officials in bringing about improvements.

In addition to *The Attendant,* one of the first of the specific experiments under the Mental Hygiene Program was put into effect in the summer of 1944, when the superintendent of the Connecticut State Hospital at Middletown, Connecticut, appointed one of the participants in the Program as full-time public relations officer for the hospital. Although heretofore an occasional hospital superintendent had welcomed the press, as far as is known, this was the first full-time public relations office in any mental hospital. (It is interesting that this particular innovation occurred in one of the hospitals where Clifford Beers had been a patient forty years before, and where he had dreamed his dreams of how he would tell the public about the true conditions and the reforms he would some day bring about.)

With doors open to the press, and without attempting to cover up shortcomings, the hospital now took the public into its confidence, asking only for a fair interpretation of its problems. Reporters and editors throughout the state were grateful for a source of news previously denied them, and they did their share in presenting a sympathetic picture of the hospital's plight, a new departure from the attitudes of suspicion and resentment then prevalent between press and public on the one side and mental hospitals on the other.

From the beginning of their work in mental hospitals, the conscientious objectors had been collecting first-hand reports about conditions. They were supported in this by a letter from Dr. George S. Stevenson, Medical Director of the National Committee for Mental Hygiene, to the superintendents of the hospitals soliciting their co-operation. By 1946, they had some fourteen hundred reports along with a collection of photographs more dramatic than words could ever be. They envisaged these reports and pictures as the backlog of an eventual "Report to the Nation" but meanwhile put them to use by making them available to writers, journalists, and other key people willing to use them constructively.

Their biggest press break came in 1946, when the editors of *Life,* stimulated by pictures the men had presented, decided to do a feature story. The *Life* article, "Bedlam, U.S.A.," came out in May 1946 and was reprinted as the lead article entitled "The Shame of Our Mental Hospitals" in *Reader's Digest* in July. One of the compelling photographs the men had given the *Life* editors, and which was used in the article and has since been reproduced countless times, showed half a dozen naked, emaciated men huddled against a peeling plaster wall, defeat, despair, degradation, crying out from every line and shadow — stark human misery at its nadir.

These two articles, appearing in two of the magazines with widest circulation in the United States, triggered a volcano of exposés and feature articles in other magazines and the daily press which continued for several years.

PRESS

Press exposés are an old story to mental institutions. One recalls Nellie Bly, the *New York World*'s extraordinary "girl correspondent" who in 1887 had herself committed to the New York City Lunatic Asylum and later wrote a lurid series "revealing asylum horrors." Nor was Nellie's either the first or the last such escapade. Many reporters before her and since have made their way into mental hospitals either as patients or employees, and it is part of the tragedy that conditions in mental hospitals have invariably been such as to provide "good copy."

But even when heartbreakingly accurate, such exposés in the past had rarely brought about lasting reforms. All too often they had been motivated not by sincere outrage and determination to improve matters (as they sometimes pretended) but by pure sensationalism. And all too often they had resulted not in inspiring people to constructive action but in frightening and alienating them and in further demoralizing overburdened public officials most of whom (though not all) were struggling to do the best they could with insufficient funds and against public indifference.

A distinguishing mark of the flood of exposés in the 1940's was that whether initiated by journalists, or by organized mental health and other civic groups (the conscientious objectors directly stimulated several), they were carried through with the co-operation of hospital staffs, medical leaders in the community, and public officials. One newspaper after another all over the country produced thoughtful, carefully planned series (they were usually series, not just single or occasional articles) describing conditions in its own state and making recommendations for reform.

For instance, Walter Lerch's series in the *Cleveland Press* influenced a subsequent reorganization of the entire state system. Albert Deutsch's series "The Shame of the States," which began in the New York daily newspaper *PM* in 1945 and was continued in the *Star,* was the most comprehensive journalistic survey of mental hospitals ever to be published, and for several years was widely used by editors and reporters as a guide for reportorial surveys in their own localities. Later Deutsch's series on veterans' hospitals, stressing particularly the shocking conditions in psychiatric facilities, helped instigate a Congressional investigation and subsequent reform of the VA system. In Oklahoma, Mike Gorman's series for the *Daily Oklahoman* later appeared as a book condensation in the *Reader's Digest* under the title "Oklahoma Attacks Its Snake Pits." In Kansas, Charles Graham's articles in the *Kansas City Star and Times,* and John McCormally's series for the *Emporia Gazette* added fuel to the fire already raging around recent scandals exposing the incredible conditions in the Kansas state hospitals and training schools. At that time, the Topeka State Hospital had two doctors for 1850 patients, and Kansas ranked 47th among the 48 states in the ratio of doctors to patients. Within five years, backed by an aroused public opinion, and with the cooperation of consultants from the Menninger Foundation and Winter VA Hospital, the Kansas revolution was brought about.

Today Topeka State Hospital has one doctor for 19 patients, and Kansas is number one state in the doctor-patient ratio. (That success story was recounted in full in 1954 in the *Reader's Digest* under the title "They Go Home Again in Kansas.") Other states with exposés and subsequent reform programs included Maryland, Minnesota, Iowa, and Texas, to name only a few.

The publicity the exposés attracted was phenomenal. With an occasional exception, the purpose was not to smear but to bring about corrections, and it is possible to trace some of the changes in public attitude which began to be apparent in the 1940's to these public airings.

The same period saw a growth of regular "columns" and "departments" in newspapers and magazines, which were also beginning to retain people on their own staffs either as columnists or reporters; these were regarded by the paper or magazine as its "mental health experts." One of the columns which was widely read throughout the United States was the weekly column, "Parent and Child" by Catherine Mackenzie in the *New York Times Magazine*. This column had several pioneering aspects, one of which was that Miss Mackenzie not only went far out of her way to make sure her reporting was accurate in the first place, but she actually "cleared" her material with the people she interviewed — a custom of which the newspaper world took a dim view at that time, but one of the devices which gradually helped to create better relations between the press and mental health.

(As part of the effort to bring about rapprochement, in 1955, after a year's preliminary preparation, the American Psychiatric Association held a three-day conference at Swampscott, Massachusetts, on "Special Problems of Communicating Psychiatric Subject Matter to the Public." This conference was attended by some thirty or forty high-level representatives of the press, and an equal number of the more articulate among the psychiatrists. Each side had an opportunity to air its resentments against the other — why psychiatrists seem stuffy and unapproachable; why the press seems aggressive and irresponsible — and to arrive at some better principles for working relationships.)

One other interesting sign of the times (the 1940's) was to be found in the cartoons of the period. From Dr. Freud and the psychoanalytic couch to Dr. Spock and the PTA, from the *New Yorker* to the tabloids, from Thurber's dogs to "Small Fry," psychiatry and psychology came in for endless lampooning (which, however, rarely seemed terribly funny to the psychologists and psychiatrists.) As with vocabulary changes, the history of mental health might almost be traced through cartoons, reflecting as they do the ideas about behavior and human relations with which people are preoccupied and epitomizing with astounding accuracy both the core of truth and the weaknesses of the new concepts.

It was during this decade too that comic strips began to be put to use in the service of mental health. *The Attendant* had used a comic strip as a regular feature beginning in 1944. In 1950 the New York State Department of Mental Hygiene developed a booklet of "Blondie" strips adapted by Joe Musial to illustrate mental health principles. It was widely circulated and later used for some significant experiments in the effectiveness of mental health education.

RADIO AND TV

In radio, a remarkable pioneering series was "The Baby Institute," produced by Virginia McMullin and moderated by Jessie Stanton, a thirty-minute show, five days a week for a year and a half, in 1943 and 1944 on the Blue Network (now the American Broadcasting Company). The program featured discussions with outstanding authorities on the physical and psychological care of young children. Scripts were carefully prepared and subjects based on letters from mothers — some 30,000 of them received during the first year.

Radio's conservatism was notable in those days. When "The Baby Institute" wanted to use the shocking term "bowel movement" it was necessary to go over several heads to a high executive to get the rules relaxed. When the newly organized National Mental Health Foundation wanted to produce a series of recorded programs, they were up against the same thing: network policy decreed that the subject of mental illness was taboo for network presentation. The Foundation had prepared a series of eight recorded programs "For These We Speak," followed later by two other longer series. It was therefore something of a feat when the Foundation, without help from any of the networks, managed to get coverage for all three series on nearly 1,000 stations in the United States and Canada.

The first hour-long radio show to receive wide acclaim was the Columbia Broadcasting System production, "Mind in the Shadow," in 1949, a sharply documented portrayal of the shocking inadequacies of mental hospitals with commentary by Dr. William C. Menninger.

By the time TV was established there were so many mental health programs that it is hard to identify a "first," but one of the most widely seen was "Out of Darkness," a ninety-minute documentary produced by the Columbia Broadcasting System in 1956, also with commentary by Dr. William Menninger. Filmed through a one-way glass window, it showed actual psychotherapeutic sessions with a young psychotic patient, and her painful struggle toward recovery. Preceded by months of planning and developed in cooperation with the Menninger Foundation, the National Association for Mental Health, and the American Psychiatric Association, "Out of Darkness" was later repeated twice on the network, and it has also been made available for 16-mm film distribution. (A little known sequel to the television production was that when a few months later the young psychiatrist who had been treating the patient was tragically killed in an automobile accident, CBS paid for the continued psychotherapy of the patient with another psychiatrist.)

FILMS

Unquestionably the most important entertainment film about mental illness to date was the Twentieth Century Fox production, "The Snake Pit," in 1946, a dramatization of the book with the same name by Mary Jane Ward, a recovered mental patient. This was probably the first time a mental patient as leading character had been portrayed sympathetically enough for the audience to be able to identify with her. Said to have grossed eight million dollars, this film was seen by an enormous number of people and its tremendous impact at the time was apparent in many ways.

Among educational films, although there had been a scattering of single films for many years, the first notable series came from the National Film Board of Canada and was called the "Mental Mechanism Series." In this country, an early series for educational use was produced by the Mental Health Film Board beginning in 1950 in cooperation with the mental health authorities of various states and still continuing with one or two new films being produced each year. The first film of the series, and probably the best, was "Angry Boy," an interpretation of the motivation behind a child's stealing episode and the role of a child guidance clinic in helping to straighten him out. Another which has had wide distribution was "Roots of Happiness," which showed harmonious home life in a simple Puerto Rican family.

Since the late 1940's, the film libraries of state and local health departments have leaned heavily on the use of mental health films as an integral part of their health education programs. Studies of the use of films have repeatedly shown that mental health films have consistently been the ones in most demand and have played to the largest audiences.

DRAMA

Beginning in 1942, the American Theatre Wing Victory Players (later better known as American Theatre Wing Community Plays), in collaboration with the New York State Committee on Mental Hygiene of the State Charities Aid Association, developed several short dramatic sketches. The first ones were on subjects related to the war and mental health. In 1949, the American Theatre Wing Community Plays and the National Committee for Mental Hygiene developed "Temperate Zone: Three Plays for Parents about the Climate of the Home." This was the beginning of a long and highly successful series of sketches about parent-child relationships. Later, the series was broadened to include other mental health subjects. These one-act plays, which were put on by small casts on a bare stage and with no properties "except what could be carried in a knitting bag" had a remarkable history. They were (and are still being) used, by amateur and Little Theatre groups throughout the United States, often under the auspices of organized mental health groups, both voluntary and governmental. One of their greatest values is the way they stimulate discussion which, partly because of the careful construction of the plays, invariably turns out to be lively.

The method of writing the plays as developed by Vera Allen and Eugenie Chapel at the Theatre Wing (with the author of this volume serving in a consulting capacity from 1942 to 1959) represented the best type of collaboration between professional workers in mental health, with their background in the study of human behavior, and professionals in the theatre world, with their skills in "getting across." The originators of this technique are now similarly producing Plays for Living under the aegis of the Family Service Association of America.

In 1951, Nora Stirling, who had written most of the earlier sketches about family living, and the present writer were coauthors of an hour-long play, "My Name is Legion," a dramatization of Clifford Beers' autobiography, *A Mind That Found Itself.* The structure of the play was modeled after the book. The first fifty minutes described Clifford Beers' experiences and suffering very much as he had told his own story. The last ten minutes, like the appendices of the book, described the mental health movement and what needed to be done for the mentally ill and for the prevention of mental illness.

The play, originally financed by the Grant Foundation, was produced jointly by American Theatre Wing Community Plays and the National Association for Mental Health, and staged by Vera Allen. The first seven performances were put on with a Broadway cast in New York City and in neighboring cities in the spring of 1952. In the fall of 1952, the Broadway cast was sent on tour for seven weeks, and in 1953 for ten weeks playing eight shows a week in about sixty cities in twenty-one states, sponsored by state and local mental health associations. The play was

intended to fulfill three purposes: straightforward education about mental illness; publicity for the organized mental health movement; and a focus for fund-raising efforts.

THE SPREAD

It was in the late 1940's that the "bandwagon" aspects
of the mental health movement first became apparent. Any
number of different types of organizations began to want
to participate but did not always have much in the way of
background to guide them in developing a program. An
example was the Junior Chamber of Commerce (Jaycees)
who early in 1949 announced that they would conduct a
"Mental Health Week" — which in a sense was jumping
the gun because none of the appropriate mental health
organizations was at that time in a position to get behind
any kind of substantial campaign. However, after much
consultation between the National Committee for Mental
Hygiene and the National Mental Health Foundation, and
the promise of assistance from the National Institute of
Mental Health, the several organizations concerned decided to pool their resources and succeeded in producing a
very creditable first joint Mental Health Week with almost
no time for planning and no budget. Alex Sareyan who in
1950 became director of public relations for the National
Association for Mental Health, directed the first four annual Mental Health Weeks and set the pattern for subsequent Mental Health Weeks. Reflecting the widespread
emphasis on mental health rather than mental illness,
which was prevalent during this period (to be described in
the next chapter), some of the first slogans officially
adopted were "Mental health is everybody's business" and
"Build mental health — our children's birthright — the
nation's strength." Later slogans reflected the swing back to
emphasis on mental illness by using such themes as "With

your help the mentally ill can come back," and "Fight mental illness."

The idea of Mental Health Week has always been to provide a peg on which to hang a publicity and fund-raising campaign at all levels: national, state, and local. In the years since 1949, Mental Health Week has grown into a mammoth operation with millions of pieces of material annually printed and circulated in addition to extensive press, radio, and television coverage, and the participation of many thousands of volunteer workers.

In 1952, a bell was chosen as the official symbol for the citizens' mental health movement, and this has been constantly in use since then. In 1953, a three-hundred-pound bell was cast which contained some of the metal from chains and handcuffs formerly used to restrain mental patients. The bell was rung for the first time that year, and it is now rung every year to signal the opening of Mental Health Week. It carries the legend, "Cast from Shackles Which Bound Them This Bell Shall Ring Out Hope for the Mentally Ill and Victory over Mental Illness."

MENTAL HEALTH MATERIALS CENTER

By the early 1950's, so much mental health material was being produced that sheer quantity had become a problem. The market was flooded. People desirous of keeping abreast of new material were overwhelmed and confused. Not only was a great deal of the new material mediocre but also much excellent material was being wasted in that it was not reaching as wide a public as it deserved because the groups which knew the most about how to prepare good material often knew little about how to get it distributed.

In order to meet the problem, a new organization was

established, the Mental Health Materials Center, with the double function of handling large-scale distribution of mental health materials and of serving health and welfare organizations in the production and distribution of their own materials when relevant to the mental health field. The Mental Health Materials Center (also called Human Relations Aids) was incorporated in 1953 as a nonprofit agency with a board and panel of consultants prominent in mental health. The organization has been responsible for the distribution of many millions of pieces of mental health materials, primarily pamphlets, but including also books, monographs, plays, films, and other audio visual aids.

Public Education and Public Relations

Although education was a major activity of the National Committee for Mental Hygiene from its inception, and of each state and local society in turn, actually the words "public education" and "mental health education" did not come into widespread use until the 1940's. The executive secretaries of the mental hygiene societies usually had over-all responsibility for the societies' programs, including public education, and although the National Committee from time to time had a staff member assigned to education, it had no division of education. In 1948, the Ittleson Family Foundation, honoring the fiftieth wedding anniversary of Mr. and Mrs. Henry Ittleson, made a grant of $50,000.00 to the National Committee for Mental Hygiene for a program of public education in mental health, and the present writer became the first director of the Committee's newly established Division of Education in 1949.

Up to then, the National Committee's educational activities had been relatively passive in the sense that educational materials were principally prepared for and made available to those who already knew enough about the subject to seek them out. The National Committee had utilized what distribution channels seemed appropriate (such as meetings and professional journals) but, as described in the foregoing section on mass media, it had never set out aggressively to capture the large mass audience — that elusive "man-in-the-street" who had never heard of "mental hygiene." And the distinctions between the Committee's concern for professional training (of core professions), professional education (of related professions), education of the public, and public relations were less clearly drawn than they came to be later.

In the 1940's, as pressures for fund-raising increased, one began to hear the expression, "We must educate people to give," which was at first used without recognition of the fact that a new twist was being given to the word "education." Translated, the phrase meant, "We must utilize public relations techniques," which was exactly what did come to be said as public relations was more and more recognized as the interpretive arm of fund-raising.

At first much confusion arose because of the failure to see the ways in which public education and public relations are similar and the ways in which they are different. Both attempt to "communicate" and both use the same media. The two may be thought of as intersecting circles with a portion of their goals held in common, but each with certain goals not shared to the same degree by the other. However, whereas education strives to purvey objective knowledge, the reason-for-being of public relations is to develop a favorable image of an organization or field in order to gain acceptance for it in the public mind. Although straightforward education is part of its armamentarium, public relations also utilizes a variety of other devices to impress or to persuade.

Public Relations and Fund-raising

As momentum built up during the 1940's, state and local executives, previously merely restive and complaining, became desperate. Their very existence was threatened because of their inability to increase or even to meet their budgets. They clamored for help in public relations as an aid to their fund-raising efforts.

The National Committee for Mental Hygiene, which had never developed public relations and fund-raising campaigns after the manner of some of the other national health organizations, was not geared to give the state and local groups the help they were now demanding. Voices both within and without the National Committee became more articulate in urging stepped-up public relations and fund-raising activities. Consequently, in a relatively short period of time, public relations and fund-raising skills came to be recognized as necessary adjuncts to the programs of mental health associations.

Points of View

Opinions differ as to exactly how public relations techniques can best serve the mental health movement. Those who fear overemphasis say that although the purpose of public relations is interpretation in order to gain public acceptance, this goal tends to become clouded if there is too much stress on publicity for its own sake. They fear that groups may tend to shape their programs to the exigencies of their publicity and fund-raising requirements (as does happen), and point to situations in which the fund-raising and public relations activities of an association have absorbed a disproportionate amount of the energy of staff and board and also of the campaign income.

Those who want to see public relations techniques utilized still more extensively than they are point to the great wave of public interest in recent years which, they say, could never have been achieved without public relations skills. They insist that the mental health movement must become a true mass movement and that only through public relations techniques is it possible to carry the message to *all* the people.

Both points of view have some justification. Public relations of the type that is excessively aggressive and opportunistic does a disservice to the field. Conducted knowledgeably, sensitively, and with complete integrity, public relations is one of the indispensable weapons in the fight against mental illness.

XIII

A Nucleus but No Boundary

The Organized Citizens' Movement

ALTHOUGH THE word "first" is used often in this account, each time it is with a qualm on the part of the writer, because again and again it happens that when one knows the full history of a development, one finds that what seemed to be a "first" was merely a logical next step, if not an outright repetition, of something comparable that went before. Tracing forerunners of forerunners — an absorbing and a humbling pursuit — sometimes makes one wonder, "*Are* there any firsts?" We therefore offer here a bow of apology to the many unsung pioneers whose early successes and failures have laid the foundation for what we now blandly label "firsts" and who are not receiving the credit which is their due for their struggles and their accomplishments.

Who knows, for instance, how much of the dogged determination of Dorothea Lynde Dix in laying her dismal discoveries before state legislatures may have prepared the ground for Clifford Beers' later work (although it is doubtless accurate to say that the modicum of citizen support Dorothea Dix mobilized here and there was scarcely of a nature to be called a "movement"). One wonders too about the role played by little-known earlier organizations such as the "Society for Improving the Condition of the Insane" in England in 1842 and the "National Association for the Protection of the Insane and the Prevention of Insanity" in the United States from 1872 to 1888.

BEFORE 1908

Among the forerunners of the present organized citizens' movement was the aftercare work of the State Charities Aid Association in New York State in the late 1800's and early 1900's, under the direction of two titans of welfare, Homer Folks and Louisa Lee Schuyler, community-minded granddaughter of Alexander Hamilton. (Like Beers and Salmon, those two were another "great team.") From the time she first organized the State Charities Aid Association in 1872, Miss Schuyler had occasion to observe the plight of the mentally ill in her "visitations" to county poorhouses, and she and Mr. Folks set the patterns for much of the Association's subsequent honorable history in the fight to aid the mentally ill. For instance, in 1885, the Association helped develop the first training course given to nurses for the insane; and in 1890, it was instrumental in bringing about the law and the appropriations providing state care and maintenance for all the insane in New York State.

In 1906, the State Charities Aid Association established a "Sub-Committee on the After-Care of the Insane" which, in 1908, was changed to the "Sub-Committee on Prevention and After-Care." (The word "after-care" in those days had some of the same connotation as our word "rehabilitation"today.) The Committee's paid social worker who worked with cases of "threatened mental disorder" was one of the first, perhaps the first paid psychiatric social worker in this country, although antedating the establishment of psychiatric social work as a profession. In 1910, the Committee became the Committee on Mental Hygiene of the State Charities Aid Association, the third of the state societies to be organized. Later, its name was changed to the New York State Committee on Mental Hygiene of the State Charities Aid Association, and it is now the New York State Association for Mental Health.

EARLY SOCIETIES

The first chapter has already recounted how Clifford Beers organized the Connecticut Society for Mental Hygiene in 1908, the first of the independent state societies, and how he planned it as a trial balloon preliminary to launching a national movement. In the early days, the Connecticut Society (now the Connecticut Association for Mental Health) was responsible for significant innovations in areas such as legislative reform, "after-care," and "free clinics," and it has continued a progressive program, but limitations of space make it impossible to report the Association's activities here. In 1958 it celebrated its fiftieth anniversary in a manner Clifford Beers would have approved, with Mrs. Beers cutting the birthday cake, and many dignitaries paying tribute to its historic role.

The second state society to be organized was Illinois in 1909, the same year the National Committee for Mental Hygiene was organized. Then the expanded New York Committee became the third in 1910. Massachusetts, Maryland, North Carolina, and Pennsylvania all came along

together in 1913. By 1914 there were enough state societies to warrant a meeting — the first meeting of state
societies — which was held in Baltimore. From then on,
each year usually saw a few more societies added to the
list, some of them representing states, some of them sections of states, and some cities or counties.

By the 1930's, there were about fifty state and local societies, more or less. By the late 1940's, there were thought
to be some two hundred societies all together, but no accurate count would have been possible during that period,
partly because of the difficulty of defining exactly which
organizations deserved to be called active mental hygiene
societies. A portion of them existed more on paper than in
reality, and they differed widely in structure, in auspices,
in program, and of course in effectiveness. Comparatively
few had paid staffs and those which did could rarely boast
more than one or at most two professional staff members
and a secretary or two. Some societies consisted of self-
perpetuating committees with relatively static programs,
satisfied to do little more than hold annual meetings.
Many of them were going through experimentation in
how to get things done and in learning what was appropriate and inappropriate for a mental hygiene society to undertake. (For instance, earlier, several had to go through
the throes of trying to operate a child guidance clinic before it was fully appreciated that mental hygiene societies
are never proper auspices for clinics.) An important few of
the societies were exceedingly lively organizations with
active subcommittees able to make themselves felt in the
community, and *all* of them, individually and collectively,
were the proverbial voice in the wilderness crying out to a
public which chose not to hear.

The state and local societies were completely autono-
mous with respect to each other and to the National Com-

mittee for Mental Hygiene. Although the National Committee encouraged states and locals to organize, and made recommendations about their programs, there was nothing resembling mandates from the national office as to what types of activities the state and locals should include in their programs. Similarly, the state and local groups felt no responsibility to the national office for financing or for program, or even for reporting what they were doing.

From Mental Hygiene to Mental Health

Some time in the late 1930's or early 1940's there occurred another of those changes in vocabulary which indicate a change in point of view: people began to dislike the word "hygiene." It had unpleasant connotations, they said. "Health" was a nicer word. They seemed (quite erroneously) to equate "mental *hygiene*" with "mental *illness*." Mental hygiene societies began to say they were not interested "just in mental illness" but in "positive mental health." The words and the idea took hold to such an extent that within comparatively few years most mental hygiene societies had changed their names from "Mental Hygiene Society" to "Mental Health Association," and mental hygiene is a term now rarely heard. Actually, however, "mental hygiene" and "mental health" never were synonymous. "Mental health" means a state or condition of health; "mental hygiene" means a body of knowledge about the preservation and promotion of mental health — a useful term and a regrettable loss.

However indefensible the change in words may have been, the change in emphasis was understandable and, as is the case with many important changes, was a resultant of multiple forces. One of these was the sincere desire to work toward prevention, an aspiration in harmony with the medical and scientific progress of the age. People looked about them, saw the miseries of mental illness, and wanted to do something more constructive than "care and treatment." In line with other scientific ideals, they wanted to get back to causes — to prevent. Because the new knowledge about human behavior was constantly stressing the ways in which mental and emotional maladjustments were traceable to environmental factors, people were eager to apply their new understanding to the improvement of environment, which took them very far afield indeed.

But there were also other forces more subtle. One of these might be described as a giving-in to the public's resistance to the subject of mental illness. Exhausted by their fruitless struggle against public apathy about the welfare of the mentally ill and seeing how much easier it was to catch public attention with the "mental health angle," the boards and staffs of mental hygiene societies could scarcely be blamed for shifting their programs away from mental illness and in the direction of mental health, especially when this could so easily be rationalized as the more important direction because they felt it implied prevention.

The effects of the change were far-reaching. In many mental health association programs, the mentally ill were all but forgotten. True, those associations would have defended their programs by saying that through their efforts for mental health they were "combatting mental illness" which is (hopefully) accurate, but the fact remained that patients who were already mentally ill were being neglected and maltreated under conditions intolerable in a humane nation, while the organized movement which was supposed to be coming to their aid was devoting only a fraction of its attention to their cause.

In recent years some of the focus on the care and treatment of the mentally ill has been restored and the total mental health movement, though retaining the broader concept of mental health, can no longer be accused of stressing mental health to the neglect of the still unsolved problems of mental illness and mentally ill people.

Another complication in the field is traceable to the ambiguity of the term "mental health" which has repeatedly proved to be a direct cause of conflict and confusion. "Mental health" is a vast term with a vast number of potential meanings, as evidenced by the fact that hundreds of definitions can be cited but there is no single accepted definition. No two qualified professional workers would define "mental health" in exactly the same way — and if there is any question on that score let the reader make a few inquiries and find out for himself. Again and again it happens that a group of people plan together in a mental health organization, using the same words but without realizing they are talking about different things. This presents a practical problem because they not only have trouble in agreeing on program priorities but some groups negate the efforts and accomplishments of other groups. Thus emerges a picture of groups having the same long-term goals but different short-term goals, and different notions about how to get where they want to go. Consequently, they fail to pull together and fail to achieve what they might if there were sharper definition of their field, and agreement on what it should *not* include as well as on what it should include. Mental health has been accurately described as a field with a nucleus but no boundary — a condition that will probably continue to plague it so long as the term "mental health" continues in use.

MERGER

The three organizations which in 1950 merged to form the National Association for Mental Health were the Psychiatric Foundation, the National Mental Health Foundation, and the National Committee for Mental Hygiene.

The Psychiatric Foundation had been organized by the American Psychiatric Association in collaboration with the American Neurological Association a few years before as the fund-raising arm of the APA, charged particularly with raising enough money to finance the hospital surveys and hopefully with enough left over for additional activities the APA wanted to undertake. The Foundation had no program of its own and actually never did get off the ground. Since, however, some of its purposes were similar to those of the other two organizations and since its fund-raising efforts were likely to compete with those of the others, it was agreed that the Foundation belonged in the merged organization.

The National Mental Health Foundation (whose origins have already been described), by 1950, was energetically pursuing the several main themes it thought most important, especially alerting the public to conditions in mental hospitals through an extensive campaign of public education and public relations, and improving the caliber of psychiatric aides. Early in their organization efforts, the founders had enlisted the support of many prominent people — Justice Owen J. Roberts, Rufus Jones, Clarence Pickett, and Mrs. Eleanor Roosevelt, to mention a few — names reminiscent in terms of public service of those who had supported the movement in its early days. All members of the staff of the Foundation were young men, most of them previously conscientious objectors, and strongly committed to their goals. At the time of the merger, the executive director was Richard C. Hunter.

The National Committee for Mental Hygiene, whose activities and accomplishments have been described throughout this account, had always retained its "committee" structure in that membership was by invitation. There were some thousand or so members, both lay and professional, who had been selected because of previously demonstrated leadership in the mental health movement. (When a person was elected to membership, he received a citation setting forth the reasons why he was being honored with this distinction.) In addition, there were several thousand contributors, many of them faithful repeaters year after year and most of them giving in amounts ranging from $1.00 to $10.00, occasionally up to $100.00, but only in the rarest instance exceeding $500.00. The general budget of the Committee was financed in this manner, and special projects were usually financed by foundation grants. The fund-raising was carried on quietly by one member of the professional staff and a few clerical workers, but there was no major fund-raising "campaign." Some of the Committee's truly distinguished achievements against great odds speak for themselves in the history of the mental health movement.

The amalgamation of the three organizations was brought about in September 1950, with Oren Root appointed president (meaning in this instance that he was the full-time paid executive director) and George S. Stevenson, M.D., as medical director. Integrating the points of view of three organizations as diverse as these was not a simple matter, and for several years the new organization labored under severe merger pains.

In the years since the merger, the National Association for Mental Health has placed much emphasis on public relations, fund-raising, and the organization of state and local associations, and it has taken on a structure entirely different from that of its predecessors, although there is not yet agreement as to exactly what the structure ought to be. Some of the present leaders prefer to regard the Association less as a national organization with a program ("program" always used here in the sense of direct activities on behalf of the mentally ill and the promotion of mental health) of its own, and more as the national office of a network of state and local organizations — in effect, a federation. Others believe it should be a truly national organization but with its program democratically and sensitively fashioned in harmony with the wishes of its affiliated associations. Still others are convinced of the necessity of a strong central program at the national level, stressing the fact that in the field of mental health, specific and unique functions and responsibilities must be carried at each level — local, state, and national — after the manner of a partnership which agrees upon a division of labor.

The National Association now provides a "national umbrella" of publicity to assist state and local organizations in their fund-raising. In return, it requires from its affiliated state associations a specified percentage of the gross income from their fund-raising campaigns, and expects the states in their turn to require a portion of the campaign-income of their affiliated local associations.

MENTAL HEALTH ASSOCIATION STAFF COUNCIL

Because of the rapid growth of the mental health movement and the shortage of trained people, many of the staff members of mental health associations have in recent years been recruited from other lines of endeavor such as community organization, public relations, group work, administration, and fund-raising. While these workers (there are some 250 executives of mental health associations in the United States) have brought an important kind of competence to their positions, many of them have not had an opportunity to secure the training they need to carry the full responsibility for the program activities demanded by their key positions. In order to cope with this problem, a new organization was created in 1957, the Mental Health Association Staff Council, with a membership consisting exclusively of staff members of mental health associations, and with the stated purpose of providing for the exchange of knowledge and experience among associations.

Where Are We Now?

Some Reasons for Optimism—with Caution

THAT THIS slender book is not attempting to describe the current scene in the mental health movement has already been explained in the preface. To do justice to the myriad activities under way would require many more pages than have gone before. And yet this account seems incomplete without at least some attempt at a brief over-all view of status and trends. Points selected for discussion are: improvement in the care of the mentally ill; changing attitude of the public; and the permeation of mental health ideas.

THE CARE OF THE MENTALLY ILL

Thousands of mental patients in the United States are getting better care than they ever had before. Happily, this fact is now incontrovertible. It is supported not just by general impressions, but by countless official reports and by statistics.

Tremendously significant is the fact that in 1956 the number of patients in mental hospitals in the United States decreased, and the downward slant has continued through 1960. To be sure, decrease in state hospital population alone is not necessarily a good thing, since it might mean merely a change in admission or discharge policy, or that patients who ought to be in hospitals were outside. In this instance, however, there is no question that it is a favorable sign. In many states, the median length of stay of patients is being reduced so that, despite increased admissions, the patient load is decreasing. This is attributed to a combination of factors, among them the large-scale use of drugs, intensive treatment of new patients, milieu therapy, and open-ward policies.

When the 1956 statistics were first announced, interpretations were cautious. Would the new figures a few years from now look like just another squiggle on the two-century upward curve? Or was this finally at last a true turning point? It is still too soon to be absolutely sure. But the picture looks hopeful. Perhaps at last we are seeing nationwide the effects of the "total push" in psychiatric care. Perhaps future historians will record the 1956 turn as one of the most significant events of the twentieth century.

But even while granting these statistics as cause for rejoicing, it is necessary to keep the whole picture of hospital care in perspective. Psychiatrists closest to the patients in the hospitals keep reminding us of certain hard realities: that in the United States, for instance, there is still only one doctor to nearly two hundred patients in our big mental hospitals, an average of well under an hour of a doctor's time per patient per month. (Is this medicine?) As to costs, the national average is still about $3.50 to $4.00 a day for mental patients, with some states below $2.00 a day, and none over $7.00, whereas it takes $25.00 to $30.00 a day to run a bed in a general hospital exclusive of medical attention. In many mental hospitals, there is a little core of heroic, dedicated doctors who are doing the best they can to treat a tenth of their hospital population while the other nine-tenths vegetate, waiting to die. We dare not congratulate ourselves on "progress" based on reports of success with the one-tenth if we keep on forgetting the nine-tenths.

As to the future, it is to be hoped that some of the changing concepts of what constitutes good care will speed better care. State mental hospitals are not inevitably and automatically the best way to care for mental patients. The entire cluster of concepts centered around state hospital care is now being challenged. For decades, not only the quality of care but the huge size and the isolation of state mental hospitals has been widely deplored. But now it is the basic idea itself which is under scrutiny. There is more than a beginning of acceptance of the conviction that even at its best state hospital care is bad for many patients; that it is indefensible to continue a system which does injury to the patients it is established to help; that mental hospitals can be valuable social institutions only if they are restricted to caring for patients they do not harm and are relieved of those who can be better cared for elsewhere; that alternatives to hospital care and methods of redistributing patients must be devised — and quickly.

The American people are being confronted with a series of dilemmas. They are recognizing the failures of past centuries. They are seeing that what they thought of as solutions, such as more and bigger hospitals — even better ones — may not be solutions at all. As they learn more and more about the deplorable facts, their own humanitarian impulses are aroused. Yet painful practical problems emerge at the same time. Startling figures are thrown at them constantly: that one-half our country's hospital beds are occupied by patients in mental institutions; that one person in ten born in the United States (or one in twelve — or fifteen — the exact figure has never been worked out) will spend some part of his life in a hospital for the mentally ill; that some states spend more than one-third of their total state budget for the care of the mentally ill. People ponder such figures against a background of facts and fears about rising costs, inflation, and "population explosion." These are worrisome considerations for the conscientious citizen.

Many of the measures proposed for relieving pressures on hospitals and improving care of patients are by now familiar to readers:

Psychiatric services in general hospitals;

In mental hospitals, more flexible patterns such as "open-door" hospitals, day hospitals, night hospitals, small regional hospitals, voluntary commitments;

Family care and nursing homes;

Rehabilitation programs to serve the needs of convalescent and discharged patients;

Community facilities of many kinds including the full range of outpatient clinical services for children and adults, and the steady development of responsibility at the level of the local community;

Earlier and more effective work by related professions.

Then, as local communities gradually assumed more responsibility, more patients would be kept in the community in the first place, or if removed, more of them would be returned in shorter time than is the case now, thereby relieving the state government of a sizable portion of its present burden of custodial care. Along with its traditional responsibility for financial assistance, the state could then devote more attention to consultative and coordinating functions: setting standards, channeling funds, and conducting demonstrations, experimentation, education, and research.

(It seems pertinent to comment here that there is nothing "new" about the concept of community responsibility for the mentally ill. "Old" concepts are being challenged, only to be replaced by still older ones. The fact that at last in this country we are beginning to develop methods of patient care which belong to history is less a compliment to modern knowledge than a reminder of how much other times and other cultures have to teach us.)

Beyond the matter of the care and treatment of mental patients, certainly no problem can be greater than finding the causes of psychotic breakdown. To this end, more funds for research are becoming available, more activity is being mobilized, and scientists assure us leads are promising. There is every reason to expect that the history of the next fifty years of the mental health movement will be able to report many new and significant results.

ATTITUDE OF THE PUBLIC

Changes in public attitude are apparent everywhere: in the mandates of the people to their government; in their voluntary organized efforts; and in their spontaneous expressions of interest and concern.

When Congress repeatedly appropriates more funds for the budget of a federal agency than the President requests for the agency, even allowing for the possibility of a little skillful lobbying some place along the line, genuine public support is almost surely indicated, and that is what has happened for several consecutive years in connection with the budget of the National Institute of Mental Health. The expanding activity of government as the instrument of the people has been recounted in an earlier chapter. In 1958, an opinion poll indicated that next to education, the American people are more willing to be taxed for the care of the mentally ill than for any other major public service. What a change since 1908!

Concomitantly has come the growth in the voluntary effort as sketched all too briefly in the chapter on the citizens' movement. The National Association for Mental Health reported that in 1960, in addition to the state mental health associations, there were some eight hundred affiliated local mental health associations in forty-two states, with a total registered membership and volunteer participation exceeding one million. This impressive evidence of the accelerated pace of the voluntary mental health effort is one of the reasons for optimism, even if progress in other directions seems slow when measured against the needs of the mentally ill and the hopes and ideals of those who care.

Up to now, the path of the voluntary mental health movement has been strew with stumbling stones. Some of these are the same ones that beset all efforts on behalf of health and welfare, and indeed the entire democratic process. An example is the snarls in which groups become entangled when problems of structure and relationship (committees and bylaws, meetings, financing, power and status prerogatives) — the machinery for action, the means to ends — are allowed to obscure the final ends of the group, their purpose, their actual reason for being.

Other stumbling stones are peculiar to the mental health movement. One is the disconcerting ambiguity of the concept "mental health," which has already been discussed at some length. Another is traceable to the special anxieties and resistances evoked by the subject, a subject, moreover, in which every man inclines to regard himself as an authority. Still another is the complexity of the field, which invariably proves harder to interpret than is usually anticipated, as attested by its checkered history.

All these factors and others have combined to create exceptional difficulties for voluntary citizen efforts. It is to their credit that mental health associations have accomplished as much as they have, and it is to be hoped that the great body of experience they are now accumulating will facilitate the effectiveness of mental health associations in the future.

PERMEATION OF IDEAS

The story of the spread of ideas about mental illness and mental health has already been recounted: the increase in the news value of the subject, utilization of the mass media, the proliferation of literature both popular and professional, the growth of professional associations and self-organizing groups, and the incorporation of mental hygiene content into higher education and professional training.

Some of the ways in which ideas about mental illness have penetrated the thinking of people to the extent of changing their behavior have been described in the preceding paragraphs which summarized the evidence of increasing concern for the mentally ill and stepped-up activities on their behalf. Another sign of public concern not previously mentioned is the fact that questions pertaining to the coverage of mental illness in health insurance plans have become one of the controversial issues of the day. Another bit of evidence corroborated by many observers is that many people seem to feel less shame than heretofore about having experienced a mental breakdown or about having a patient in the family; they seem to have a clearer conception of what mental illness is, a willingness to admit it and discuss it, and to accept psychiatric help when required — altogether a much healthier attitude.

The extent to which ideas about mental health (in contradistinction to mental illness) have permeated people's thinking, though more difficult to demonstrate, is equally dramatic and perhaps potentially even more constructive. Certainly there is now widespread acceptance of such "mental health principles" as the fact that behavior is caused, that the causes are multiple, that emotions and unconscious drives are powerful motivating forces, that the satisfaction of basic physical, psychological, and social needs is essential to healthy development, and that early life experiences contain significant determinants of later adjustment.

There is evidence of more and more reaching out for knowledge about interpersonal relations, of more awareness of the need for understanding motivation in order to cope with many of our current social ills, and of a constant search for depth in the interpretation of the dynamics of human behavior.

People long not only for help with their problems but for positive goals of living. Although some of these are shared with ethics, philosophy, religion, and education (the distinctions are not always clear — that ambiguity bugaboo again), nevertheless to some of them mental health has a special contribution to make. It offers as an ideal a concept of high-level-wellness. A widely used leaflet entitled "Mental Health Is. . . . 1, 2, 3," first published by the National Association for Mental Health in 1951, describes the characteristics of mentally healthy people: "They feel comfortable about themselves; they feel right about other people; they are able to meet the demands of life."

The field of mental health strives to bring to bear scientific information on the age-old problems of love and hate, fear and tension and anxiety; human aspirations and failures; man's relations to his fellow man including his inhumanity; his war with himself — in short the entire gamut of human behavior. To attain its goals, the body of knowledge about mental health must not be limited to any one profession or group of professions, but must be incorporated into the body of knowledge of all the helping professions and all those who work with people. Its success must be measured not by specific accomplishments for or by a few groups, but by the effectiveness with which its ideas are taken over into the work of others and finally become part of the knowledge and understanding of more and more people. That is what is actually happening — and that is another of the reasons for optimism.

Bibliography

Of the many books, articles, pamphlets, and reports which have been drawn on in the preparation of this account, three books have been helpful above all others: several different editions of Clifford Beers' book, *A Mind That Found Itself*, with their invaluable historical appendices (Longmans Green, New York, 1908; Doubleday, New York, 1931, 1948, 1953); Albert Deutsch's incomparable *The Mentally Ill in America* (Doubleday, New York, 1937); and Earl D. Bond's *Thomas W. Salmon: Psychiatrist* (Norton, New York, 1950), a book which brings to life the movement as it was in its early days.

Other valuable and relevant histories used were: *Child Guidance Clinics: A Quarter Century of Development* by George S. Stevenson and Geddes Smith (Commonwealth Fund, New York, 1934); *One Hundred Years of American Psychiatry*, published for the American Psychiatric Association (Columbia University Press, 1944); and *Orthopsychiatry 1923–1948: Retrospect and Prospect,* edited by Lawson G. Lowrey (American Orthopsychiatric Association, 1948).

The reader who wishes to pursue current developments may be interested in the two-volume (2,100 double-column pages!) *American Handbook of Psychiatry* (Basic Books, New York, 1959) edited by Silvano Arieti and a board of editors with 111 contributing authors; this book undertakes to present "the development, concepts, trends, techniques, problems and prospects of psychiatry today, in a form useful for both the expert and the beginner, in which every leading school of thought and every major approach is included."

Particularly relevant to the current status of the mental health movement is the ten-volume series of reports on the findings of the Joint Commission on Mental Illness and Health created by Congress under a Mental Health Study Act in 1955, which provided a mandate to assess mental health conditions and resources throughout the United States. The Commission, under the chairmanship of Jack Ewalt, M.D., was established as a nongovernmental, multidiscipline, nonprofit organization representing a variety of national agencies concerned with mental health. The monographs, each one by a different author, are issuing from the press as this is being written (Basic Books, 1959 and 1960). Subjects include current concepts of positive mental health, economics of mental illness, manpower trends, sampling survey of mental health, the role of schools, research resources, religion and mental health, community resources, epidemiology of mental illness, and the care of mental patients.

Acknowledgments

Although this is a slight piece of work in number of pages, writing it presented extraordinary difficulties. The more than forty authorities who were kind enough to read the manuscript were generous with their assistance far beyond what was asked of them. To each one of them I wish to express my sincere gratitude.

I hasten to make the usual author's disclaimer on behalf of the critics: although they contributed immeasurably to making this a better manuscript, I assume full responsibility for errors of fact or interpretation; and while on the whole their approval was gratifying beyond all expectation, the fact that their assistance is acknowledged is not intended to imply that all of them agreed with all points of view expressed here.

William C. Menninger, M.D., President of the Menninger Foundation, in addition to his gracious introduction, earlier wrote several long letters of comment which are veritable historical documents in themselves. George S. Stevenson, M.D., formerly Medical Director of the National Association for Mental Health and its predecessor, the National Committee for Mental Hygiene, who has probably had more to do with more of the events described here than any other one person, spent several hours on each of several occasions recalling from memory facts otherwise difficult to verify, and discussing points having to do with the sequence of events, attributions, relative emphasis, and other aspects of interpretation.

Robert Barrie, Executive Director of the New York State Association for Mental Health, and William T. Beaty, II, Assistant Executive Director, in their capacity as representatives of the sponsoring agency were exceedingly helpful in many different ways, and, in addition, Mr. Beaty helped to formulate the difficult final chapter. Other mental health association executives who shared their experience were John D. Griffin, M.D., General Director of the Canadian Mental Health Association; Richard C. Hunter, Executive Director of the Southeastern Pennsylvania Association for Mental Health; Merle W. Mudd, Executive Director of the Connecticut Association for Mental Health; and Loyd W. Rowland, Ph.D., Executive Director of the Louisiana Association for Mental Health.

Officials of government agencies who contributed cogent criticisms were Robert Felix, M.D., Director of the National Institute for Mental Health and President of the American Psychiatric Association; Paul M. Hoch, M.D., Commissioner of the New York State Department of Mental Hygiene; Mabel Ross, M.D., Mental Health Consultant, National Institute for Mental Health; and Marjorie Watson, formerly Chief of the Mental Hygiene Information Service, Ohio State Department of Mental Hygiene and Correction.

The historic role of the Commonwealth Fund has been mentioned a number of times, and to this organization I express gratitude for making possible the publication of this manuscript. Three executives of the Fund who made valuable suggestions about both the past and the present were John Eberhart, Ph.D., Mildred Scoville (retired), and E. K. Wickman (retired). I also wish particularly to thank Roger A. Crane, Director of the Fund's Division of Publications, for his role in bringing this book into being.

Quite a few of the critics restricted their suggestions to the sections within their special province: Vera Allen — the section on the American Theatre Wing Community Plays; Muriel Brown, Ph.D., Parent Education Specialist, (U.S.) Children's Bureau — the section on parent education; Gunnar Dybwad, J.D., Executive Director, National Association for Retarded Children — the chapter on the mentally deficient; Irving Gitlin, Program Executive, CBS News — the description of the two CBS television productions; Molly Harrower, Ph.D., Associate Professor of Research in Clinical Psychology, Temple University — the section on the development of clinical psychology; Earl A. Loomis, Jr., M.D., Director of the Program in Psychiatry and Religion, Union Theological Seminary — the section on religion and psychiatry; John R. Rees, M.D., Director of the World Federation for Mental Health — the chapters on war and international activities; Robert L. Robinson, Public Information Officer of the American Psychiatric Association — details pertaining to the complicated history of the hospital surveys; Milton J. E. Senn, M.D., Sterling Professor of Pediatrics and Psychiatry at Yale University and Director of the Yale Child Study Center — the sections on child psychiatry and pediatrics; Zitha R. Turitz, Director of the Standards Project, Child Welfare League of America — the section on residential care and the last chapter.

Three authors whose books have already been mentioned as contributing importantly to the historical background in this account have placed me still further in their debt by their valuable letters of comment: Earl D. Bond, M.D., biographer of Thomas W. Salmon; Stanley P. Davies, Ph.D., author of *The Social Control of the*

Mentally Deficient, and Albert Deutsch, author of *The Mentally Ill in America.*

In addition to the several psychiatrists mentioned above, other psychiatrists who kindly reviewed the manuscript were C. Douglas Darling, M.D., Psychiatrist in the Student Medical Service, Cornell University, and Past President of the New York State Association for Mental Health; William Goldfarb, M.D., Director of the Henry Ittleson Center for Child Research; and Frank F. Tallman, M.D., Professor of Psychiatry, University of California.

Members of the staff of the Mental Health Materials Center — Isabel Johnson, Jack Neher, and Alex Sareyan, Director of the Center — were generous in sharing their impressions of the events of the past fifteen years based on their extensive experience in mental health education, public relations, and the use of the mass media.

Emily Martin, member of the staff of the National Association for Mental Health and the National Committee for Mental Hygiene since 1917, added some important details from her rich store of memories of the people and events which are the subject of this account.

Two attorneys who kindly checked the section on legal protection were Alan M. Stroock and Sidney Voletsky.

Georgia Lightbody of the Lenox School, and Alice and John Baldwin of the Northfield and Mt. Hermon Schools, made some pertinent suggestions about style.

For their interest and encouragement, a special word of thanks is due to Mrs. Clifford W. Beers, Mrs. Henry Ittleson, and Mrs. Henry Ittleson, Jr.; and to my secretary, Ida Voletsky, for her patience beyond the call of duty.

And finally, to my husband, M. Arnold Boll: appreciation which mere words cannot convey.

NINA RIDENOUR